THE SUFFERING HUMAN BEING

THE SUFFERING HUMAN BEING

Katie Eriksson

English Translation by
Karl A. Olsson
and Charles I. Peterson

Edited by
Charles I. Peterson
and Joan E. Zetterlund

Nordic Studies Press
Chicago

The Suffering Human Being

by Katie Eriksson

© Nordic Studies Press 2006

An earlier version of this book was published
in Swedish as *Den Lidande Människan*.
© Katie Eriksson and Liber AB Stockholm 1994.

Nordic Studies Press
5451 N. Christiana
Chicago, IL 60625
USA

www.nordicstudiespress.com

ISBN 0-9772714-0-4

Cover art: "Suffering," oil painting by Johan Candelin
Typeset by Double Click Design
Printed in the United States by ABC Printing Company
Chicago, IL

To mother and father
In deep reverence and thankfulness
for what you are, have been
and always will come to be

Table of Contents

Editor's Foreword

I first became aware of the work of Katie Eriksson when I was a nursing exchange faculty member in Sweden in the early 1990s. I was teaching the nursing theory course to graduate students at North Park University in Chicago, and was interested in developing a theory of caring that integrated both theology and philosophy. My colleagues in Sweden were familiar with Eriksson's work, and arranged a visit with her. I soon became aware of her important role in the development of caring science in the Nordic countries. She is one of the pioneers among the many educators and researchers from these countries who have made major contributions to caring science and to caring literature, including philosophical and theological perspectives. Much of their work has been written and published in the Nordic languages; to continue their leadership in the global expansion of caring science and caring literature requires expansion of their publications available in English. It is for this reason that the translation of this book was initiated.

Katie Eriksson is Professor and Director of the Department of Caring Science at Åbo Akademi University in Vaasa, Finland. The Department offers masters and doctoral degrees in caring science, with classes taught primarily in the Swedish language. Professor Eriksson oversees the rapidly increasing caring science research by doctoral and post-doctoral students and by faculty at the Department. As part of her professorship, she also is responsible for caring research and education at Helsinki University Central Hospital as Director of Nursing.

A prolific writer, she has published numerous professional journal articles in Swedish and Finnish, and an increasing number of them have been translated and published in English. Several of her books have been translated into other Scandinavian languages, but *The Suffering Human Being* is the first of her books to be translated into English. A comprehensive presentation of her work and a complete listing of her publications and those from the Department of Caring Science are included in the recent publication of her theory. [See Lindström, U.Å., Lindholm, L. & Zetterlund, J.E. (2006). Katie Eriksson: Theory of caritative caring. In A.M. Tomey and M.R. Alligood (Eds.), *Nursing theorists and their work* (6th ed.). St. Louis: Mosby, Inc.]

The initial translation of this book was done by Karl Olsson, Professor Emeritus and former President of North Park University. His work was nearly completed when he was seriously injured in an automobile accident from which he never fully recovered. Although he and Katie Eriksson never met in person, they were able to visit by telephone during one of our work sessions before his accident. Following Olsson's death, progress on the book was stopped for a period of time, until Charles Peterson agreed to serve as both translator and co-editor.

It is difficult in any translation work to preserve the original meaning of the text. This has been the challenge of this translation as well, because a single Swedish word or concept may have several different contextual meanings or definitions. In an attempt to be as accurate as possible, this translation is for the most part a literal one. One exception is the concept analysis discussion in Chapter 3, where some of the etymology content has been moved to the Notes, resulting in some reorganizing of the chapter. The translation text and references also follow the writing style of the original book, which may be unfamiliar to the American reader. The use of the feminine gender throughout the text and the masculine gender in the Epilogue have remained consistent with the original text.

It is impossible to acknowledge everyone who has had any part in the completion of this project. Yet there are many faculty colleagues both in Vaasa and in Chicago who have been consulted at various stages of the translation. To each of you, too many to mention by name, I extend my thanks. Competent office assistance is always essential, and I want to acknowledge the efficiency of Grace Schroeder in transcribing the major portion of the initial hand-written translation. I am also grateful to Lotta Björk for assistance in translating references and editing sections of the book, and to Ida Wikberg, for her extensive editing clarifications in the final translation. My deepest thanks to you all.

I especially acknowledge with gratitude the work of Karl Olsson in the translation of this book. I also want to thank Sally Olsson for carefully photocopying each section of the translation as it was completed by her husband, and sending them to me for transcribing. Her participation in the process, as well as her faithful support of Karl throughout the months of his work on this translation, are gratefully acknowledged.

Finally, it has been a privilege for me to have a part in making this translation possible. I thank Charles Peterson for being willing to join me in completing this venture. Together with Katie Eriksson, we hope that those who read *The Suffering Human Being* will gain a little better understanding of suffering in caring and in their own lives, and thus be better able to alleviate the suffering of others.

Joan E. Zetterlund

Author's Preface to the English Edition

The initial Swedish edition of this book, *Den Lidande Människan*, was written in the early 1990s. It was the result of a research program on health and suffering conducted by the Department of Caring Science, Åbo Akademi University in Vaasa, Finland. As our research indicates, it is evident that in health care and caring today we are about to forget the original concept of patient, which means "the suffering human being." The patient's dignity is often violated, and this causes a suffering that we call suffering related to care. This book can be seen as a defense of human dignity and as a program declaration for caring science research. To understand suffering is a prerequisite for understanding health in a deeper sense and of finding ways to alleviate suffering through caring communion based on "caritas," or love and mercy.

Through this book I have tried to speak to the suffering human being, from a suffering human being, about suffering. I have tried to speak of a suffering where hope and despair meet, where light and darkness break like waves against each other in a distant horizon, where the rays of hope illuminate the way. It is a message about life and love and about the human being's infinite potential and the all-embracing communion of love that unites human beings around the world.

It is with great humility and gratitude that I through my messengers in the USA, Charles Peterson and Joan Zetterlund, present my thoughts on suffering. I personally want to acknowledge the work of Professor Zetterlund, who was the initiator of the translation and who has been responsible for its realization. I also am especially grateful to Karl Olsson for his interest in my work and his willingness to accept the challenge of translating this book. I lack words to express my deepest and warmest thanks to You all!

Katie Eriksson

Preface to the Swedish Edition

To encounter your suffering is to enter into an infinite chain of farewells.

It has taken me several years to write this book. It has developed along-side a research project about suffering conducted by the Department of Caring Science at Åbo Akademi University in Vaasa, Finland. A partial report, *Encounters With Suffering* (Eriksson, ed.) was published in May 1993. A number of scientific articles and conference reports have also been published.

I have meditated for a long time about the name of the book. For a long time I called it *The Idea of Suffering*, and I saw the book as a contin-uation of my earlier books: *The Idea of Health* (1976, 1989), *The Idea of Caring* (1987) and *The Pause, the Idea of Caritas* (1987). I have time and again asked myself the question if suffering has an idea. My answer is that since suffering exists, it must have an idea! The idea of suffering belongs to the idea of the human being. It is the human being who suf-fers, and it is the human being who causes suffering. It is also the human being who can alleviate the suffering of the other and make it endurable. Slowly it became clear to me that the name of the book was to be *The Suffering Human Being*. To describe suffering as an abstract idea or as a phenomenon seems meaningless if it is not mirrored in a human being as the bearer of suffering. It is also the suffering human being we meet in caring and who, in the deepest meaning, motivates our caring. It is through the power of love that we can care and alleviate suffering. Where love and suffering meet, true compassion and true caring emerge.

This book is based on encounters with suffering both in literature and in real life. Infinitely much has been written about suffering, and it would be both impossible and meaningless to try to capture everything that has been written. I have chosen to present the thoughts that have developed in my encounters with suffering and through the results we have obtained in our research about suffering. In Notes I have pointed out central references without the need to cover the whole field, so that interested readers can immerse themselves in the different areas. Nev-ertheless, for the formulations and thoughts in this book I am personally responsible.

The book comprises essentially two parts. In the first part I try to describe human suffering, and in the second part I describe the suffering I have encountered in the work of caring. The book addresses itself to each and every one interested in trying to understand suffering and who has the will to seek to alleviate the suffering of a fellow human being.

There are many I want to thank who in various ways have participated in my encounters with peoples' suffering. First and foremost, there are all the patients, their families and caregivers who shared their experiences. There are all my colleagues at the Department of Caring Science, Åbo Akademi University in Vaasa, Finland: Terese Bondas-Salonen, Anette Dahlvik, Siv Herberts, Britt-Marie Högnabba, Anne Kasén, Lisbet Lindholm, Unni Å. Lindström, Dahly Matilainen, Carita Mäkelä, and Ingeborg Nyberg who have participated and shared the suffering and desire during the years we worked with the suffering project. An extra special big thank you to Britt-Marie who over and over again corrected the manuscript and to Anne who read the text and checked the references. Thanks for all that you gave!

Vaasa, in the spring

Katie Eriksson

Reflection on Suffering

The well-springs of art are love, life, and suffering. Art emerges from the human spirit and mingles with the nuances of body and soul to form a work that mirrors the innermost being of the person and the actual formation of her existence.

I want to create a symphony in major and minor keys with joy, life, suffering, sorrow and pain. Its name shall be Suffering.

I want to create a work of art from the sparkling stars of heaven and the corals of the sea. Its name shall be Love.

I want to paint a picture that contains the goodness of the whole world and its beauty. Its name shall be Compassion.

Speak to me about suffering, Your suffering. Speak so that it appears in all its uniqueness with all of its nuances and dimensions. I will try to understand and within me form a gestalt of Your suffering through my Compassion.

Chapter
One

The Universe of Suffering

When in my deepest suffering I have the strength to turn my eyes to the Milky Way, a gleam of hope is born and I dare to believe that perhaps love will conquer and that my life and my suffering will become a part of the Milky Way, the bridge of Love.

The suffering human being finds herself in a sort of universe of suffering, an infinite number of happenings that at last and despite all, are shown to have a connectedness. Suffering has often been pictured as a mystery or a riddle, but its immensity results in my wanting to call it a universe. That likeness accords every age and every person a given place in relation to suffering, since we are forced to try to understand suffering in relation to our own life and our own becoming. At the same time, there is something historically given that makes the question of suffering of current interest for us.

Suffering is appropriate for the human being. To live implies, among other things, to suffer. This book builds on the assumption that suffering is a part of all human life. Suffering is, in its deepest meaning, a form of dying. Yet, where life triumphs, suffering has constituted a source of energy for new life. Suffering is something entirely evil and does not have any meaning in itself, but each human being by passing through suffering assigns a meaning to it. Suffering is a struggle between evil and good, between suffering and desire. Life and death, suffering and desire constitute the core in all human life. Without all of this, life would be empty and without movement. Suffering is a struggle for one's dignity and one's freedom to be a human being. Every human being tries to master her suffering through sacrifice, to perform an act of reconciliation. Suffering lacks a specific language but in its infinite silence there are forms of expression that we can perceive with our innermost and most sensitive movements, our mutuality, and our compassion.

It is difficult to find a definite position regarding suffering. One moment one is prepared to see it as something definitely evil, only in the next moment perhaps to beautify it by wanting to ascribe a meaning to it. I believe that fundamentally there is a suffering that lacks all meaning. I have met that kind of suffering in my work in caring, especially among children and outcasts. At the same time I have time and again experienced a suffering that, despite everything, has a meaning. It has found meaning through the limitless love that, despite all, exists. The meaning of life and the meaning of suffering seem to belong together. When life has a meaning, suffering also can be given a meaning.

For me the universe appears as the land of possibilities. It is the vision, the land that does not exist but which nevertheless can accommodate all my dreams, my longings, and even my fears and my contempt. It is the land of love and hate where the holy and the demonic can dine at the same table. It is a fascinating and chaotic multiplicity. The universe is the picture, the moment, and the unbroken stream of life from birth to death. My life is my universe; I have no choice, for life has chosen me with its suffering and desire.

It is from these perspectives that this book has been written. Some questions are penetrated more thoroughly and others more superficially. The book is an attempt to penetrate a small part of the universe of suffering, the infinity that each and every one must experience in order to understand.

**Chapter
Two**

The *What* of Suffering

*If you try to capture your suffering,
you will be forever captive of
suffering.*

The question of the *what* of suffering is an attempt to describe the nature of suffering. The *what* of suffering is a characteristic of each separate suffering. We shall probably never get an answer to the *what* question. Suffering will presumably always appear as a riddle since each person's suffering is unique and bears the name of the sufferer. The *what* question of suffering seems to be difficult to answer. Instead of answering the *what* question we answer the *why*.[1] The answer to the *what* question of suffering we find in more personal documents such as poetry, fiction, etc. The *what* question is naturally difficult to answer since suffering, as such, lacks character. Through the *why* question the person can position suffering in relation to her own situation and to something that makes it possible to manage the suffering. Colliander writes in his book, *Motives*:

> Suffering, as such, lacks every quality, has no character, no signature. The suffering person confers on suffering its character. She gives it the color of ruin or blessing, meaning or meaninglessness. Like our dreams, our suffering is inaccessible to external scrutiny. Suffering is carried solely by the individual, never by the multitude. (Colliander 1987, 81)

All people do not have the ability to suffer. Frankl (1974) believes that the ability to suffer is essential for the human being, since suffering belongs to one of life's deepest conditions. Frankl argues that on the biological plane pain is a warning signal for the person that something is awry; this is the way suffering functions on the psychic and spiritual plane. Suffering protects us from apathy and psychic rigidity. One who tries to anesthetize one's suffering doesn't solve any problems. One can set aside an experience but not its cause. Jung presents the same idea and believes that the starting point of suffering is spiritual rigidity and the unfruitfulness of the spirit.[2]

To remove need and dying, suffering and fate from life would be to rob life of its character and form. Fate is meaningful; we must shape it when possible and endure it when necessary. There are people who cannot grieve or weep. There is probably no deeper despair than that of people who cannot grieve. For people to recognize the *what* of their suffering we must help them to recover the ability to suffer.

The Inability to Suffer

"A person suffers as long as she doesn't dare to swim in the chaotic stream of life."

Jung, Briefe I, 68

The inability to suffer is perhaps one of the greatest and cruelest of all suffering. A person who bears this inability is often exposed to the contempt of her surroundings since she does not "behave" as one who is suffering. Seen objectively she should suffer and express the pain and misfortune expected of her. When the person who, according to various objective judgments, should suffer but does not suffer, the disappointment often becomes so great that one unconsciously or consciously wants to force an expression of suffering from them.

A real inability to suffer is easily confused with other forms of expression, for example, contempt and arrogance in the face of suffering. Expressions of contempt and arrogance can in themselves be examples of human suffering, but such forms of expression must be dealt with differently than the expression of an inability to suffer.

Another variation of suffering may be found in the person who expresses a *will* to suffer and perhaps even *seeks* suffering. Many times these people encounter mistrust and are labeled as malingerers, which further increases their suffering.

Johannisson (1992) feels that there is a fundamental attitude towards suffering, self-conscious suffering, where the person's ego is the focus. Suffering, by being raised to a higher dimension or by being romanticized, can give the sufferer a special status.

In the deepest meaning no person presumably wants to suffer. Even self-conscious and apparently self-generated suffering is an expression of a more profound suffering, perhaps a life-suffering that includes feeling totally powerless over life.

Passion in Suffering

The glory of suffering is only an illusion.

In suffering that just *is* and actually does not contain any movement, there sometimes exists something that can be called passion. Passion is conceptually related to suffering. It is as if the person in her seemingly hopeless situation sometimes expresses her pain or suffering through passion. In passion there is a creative force, and by giving in to it the person may forget suffering for a period of time. One often finds expression of this tragic creativity in music, art, fiction, etc. One could say passion in suffering is a way of giving suffering a meaning. The passion itself is a suffering but through giving the suffering the signature of passion, one can at least for a while make it endurable.

Suffering as Temptation

"All suffering comes from love and inclination."

Meister Eckhart

Suffering can become a temptation for a person, an enticement and a testing that one finds difficult to resist.[3] In the face of temptation, which in its deepest meaning is obsession, the struggle increases. To resist temptation requires courage. To yield to temptation can, at least for a time, give the person satisfaction and experiences of desire, only to have it changed in a moment to suffering. A person who even briefly yields to a temptation that she cannot approve, judges herself and experiences a loss of personal dignity. Another possibility is that she feels a satisfaction in the suffering and gives in or resigns and enters into the suffering that subsequently becomes a way of life.

It is an interesting thought that Pauli (1938, 29) presents when she describes suffering as a temptation. When suffering becomes a temptation, it easily creates bitterness and indifference for everything and everyone. This makes the person lose courage, weakens her in every respect and leads to premature aging.

Suffering – A Form of Dying

"In the act to annihilate, the pain is increased." [4]

In its deepest meaning suffering is a form of dying.[5] In each suffering something definitive is taken from us in concrete or symbolic meaning. Each suffering can be likened to a struggle with death. In suffering there is sorrow over what we have lost or are about to lose. Suffering implies that the human being can be transformed, created or disintegrated. In dying there is a possibility for new life, i.e., reconciliation. If reconciliation cannot be experienced, a quiet death ensues where the soul and spiritual life most often die first.

In suffering that causes death, the human being is obliterated as a person and a whole human being. She is disintegrated by hopelessness, sorrow, guilt, humiliation, and loneliness. In the absence of confirmation of her worth as a human being, she enters a world that is far beyond all relationships and thus beyond all suffering. In the world where the human being is no longer a person, suffering does not exist. The suffering, the guilt, and the pain may be found in the next of kin or the people who stand in a close relationship to the "dying" human being.

In suffering there is sorrow and grief. Kallenberg (1992, 139) sees sorrow as a form of suffering and asks: "If grieving is a form of suffering, what meaning does suffering have?" He means that suffering has no meaning in itself, but it can be seen as a phase in personal growth and development. The events that cause the grief lack meaning, but a meaning can emerge eventually. Kallenberg alludes to Freud's thoughts on "grief work" and analogically with Kierkegaard's (1928) thought that the person wearies of suffering. A person who suffers and grieves is tired. A tired person needs rest and calm but not necessarily solitude. A person who definitely has lost a person she loves and who has been important to her, experiences a great loneliness. The deepest feeling of loneliness is perhaps not to be seen by anyone. Perhaps this is also the deepest suffering? Not to be seen is to be considered as "dead." Unfortunately, there are many living-dead among us. We encounter these suffering fellow human beings daily, but we fail to see them. We meet these people in our hospitals, but they are also in the midst of us.

NOTES

[1] The difficulty in describing the *what* question of suffering emerges in the empirical studies carried out in a research project on suffering at the Department of Caring Science, Åbo Akademi University. See Eriksson (ed. 1993) *Encounters with Suffering*. The question as such is not discussed in the literature.

[2] See Jung, *Die Gesammelte Werken* , II, 340, and Jung (1993).

[3] *Temptation* is not given as a synonym for *suffering*. On the other hand there is a connection between *testing* (given as a synonym for *temptation*) and *suffering*. *Obsession* is a synonym for both *suffering* and *temptation*. *Temptation* also has the synonym *enticement*, which refers directly to *desire* and *longing*. (Strömberg, 1984).

[4] I have read this text on a plaque that may be found in the entrance of a college of nursing in Sweden.

[5] According to conceptual analysis of *suffering* we get support for the idea that suffering is a form of dying. See Eriksson and Herberts (1993) and Chapter 3. That thought is given support by, among others, Stearns (1984, 96) *Living through Personal Crisis*. She differentiates between a positive suffering that strengthens the individual and a negative suffering that kills, that is, obliterates the person.

Chapter Three

The Concept of Suffering

Every concept is like a star in the Milky Way and leads us deeper into the infinite multiplicity of the universe.

The question of the nature of suffering is perhaps best clarified by a concept analysis.[1] Through concept analysis it is possible to describe the historical development of a concept and its transformation over time, and to reveal dimensions and relationships otherwise difficult to grasp. With the help of concept analysis one can make a general characterization of suffering as a concept and as a phenomenon. A concept refers to a definite *tankeinnehåll* (thought content) and every concept can be expressed in a number of terms. The terms can eventually replace the concept and lead to a change in the original thought content.

Etymological analysis of the Swedish concept *lidande (suffering)* indicates that during the last century the concept of *suffering* has shown signs of disappearing and has been replaced by a number of terms, for example: pain, anxiety, and illness, which represent different thought content. The concept of *suffering* has been desubstantiated; it has lost its original meaning both in health care and in general contexts. Recently one can clearly see a development toward reintroducing the concept of *suffering* both in the scientific literature of caring science and in fiction.

Prior to the 1920s, the Swedish concept of *suffering* did not pass through any noteworthy change of meaning in a semantic sense. *Suffering* meant pain, torment, agony and anguish. After the 1940s, especially, we can see a change in meaning so that one increasingly describes suffering as illness and pain. One sees, at the same time, within Swedish language usage, a decreased use of the concept of *suffering*. This change is supported by the literature where one describes the concept's metamorphosis and its reduction to a denotation of physical pain and diagnosis of illness.[2] It is interesting to note that *illness* emerges as a synonym for *suffering* initially in the 1930s, but according to the Swedish Academy's Dictionary Collection (SAOB Archives), *suffering* in the sense of illness occurs as early as the 17th century. The concepts of *suffering* and *pain* are not synonymous; there is *suffering* where there is no *pain*, just as there is *pain* that exists without *suffering*. The dimensions of *suffering* are presented in Figure 1.

Suffering has both a negative and a positive dimension. The opposite of *suffering* is *desire*. That there are gladness and enjoyment in suffering is supported by our concept analysis, but the positive dimensions of desire and pleasure do not emerge in the semantic analysis. Our concept analysis supports the idea of *suffering* as a form of dying:

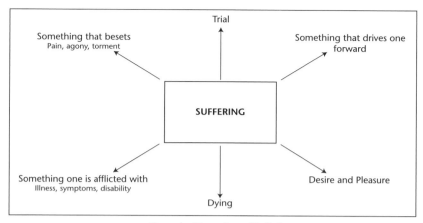

Figure 1. Dimensions of Suffering

> Every suffering is a beginning of dying, for it takes from us something on which we consciously or unconsciously support ourselves. (SAOB Archives 1906)

To Suffer

The Swedish verb *lida (suffer)* displays similarities to the noun *lidande (suffering)*. To suffer is to be *tormented* and to *suffer agony*. It is something evil that besets a person. To suffer is to *struggle* and to *endure*. But to suffer can also mean *to be reconciled*. If one looks at the etymological significance of the concept *suffering* and its meaning in other languages, one finds support for the dimensions stated above.[3] According to the *Swedish Etymological Dictionary* (Hellquist 1980) the word *lida (suffer)* means *endure* or *bear*, and is the same word as in the phrase *time passes*. The word originates in the old Swedish *lidha* meaning walk, travel and walk, time passes.

The way in which the term *suffer* is presented in SAOB coincides for the most part with the results of our semantic analysis. SAOB utilizes the phrase "provokes feelings of a certain kind, usually of sympathy for someone or something." Sympathy goes back to the Greek *sympatheia*, which can also be translated as *compassion*. One could say that compassion is a form of suffering (See Chapter 8). According to the SAOB archives, *to suffer* also can be synonymous with *desire* or an expression of something that people suffer a shortage of, or lack.

In summary, from the semantic analysis one can differentiate the following main dimensions for the concept *suffer*:

1. Something negative or evil, something that besets a person.
2. Something a person has to live with, something to which she is subjected.
3. A struggle.
4. Something constructive or carrying meaning, a reconciliation.
5. Suffering as compassion, that is, to suffer with and for someone else.
6. Suffering as the expression of something that people lack.

Suffering and Desire

The analysis of the Swedish concept *lust (desire)*, in contrast to *lidande (suffering)*, reveals the following major dimensions[4]:

1. Desire as something which drives a person; it can be compared to need.
2. Desire as a deeper longing for something; a craving, a wish or a will.
3. Desire as something life giving and positive; life, joy, and calling.
4. Desire as devotion or love for someone.

Suffering's connection to desire, joy, and pleasure appears also in the following quotation:

> Suffering and pleasure belong together…as the negative and the positive pole on a mathematical line. They require each other in order to have any understandable significance and in reality they constantly merge into each other…I take joy in my suffering for you. (SAOB Archives 1926)

There is much evidence in the literature that suffering gives birth to an unsuspected life power that is not seen as having any other source than suffering itself. The idea that suffering constitutes a positive power, which brings with it something good, has existed for a long time:

> The only thing that is able to elevate the average human being is suffering. (SAOB Archives 1903, 1906)

> …it is certain that suffering has greater power to move one forward than pleasure. (SAOB Archives 1910)

The connection between suffering and desire has meaning for our view of health and ill-health, and as we will see in Chapter 9, there is a connection between suffering and health. Desire and suffering make up the driving power for a person's being and formation into the person she is intended to become. Suffering as well as desire can become a passion or temptation and lead a person into evil and into sin. Suffering and desire can also be compared to virtue, a struggle that promotes the desire to live and to grow. (See Chapter 4)

Suffering As Sacrifice and Innocent Victim

Based on the SAOB Archives, a number of other meanings of the term *suffering* appear, including *suffering* as *sacrifice*. *Sacrifice* has a connection with martyrdom and martyr, meaning that the one who suffers offers herself for something or she becomes a sacrifice. Martyrdom is in etymological meaning identical with the Swedish *marter*, meaning victim. SAOB explains *martyrium* as an innocent victim. Originally the word *martyr* signified people who suffered a martyr's death for the sake of their faith or ideas. They were innocent victims in the sense that they were ahead of their time or deviated from convention and thereby became victims. Today the suffering patient is often the innocent victim of health care. Åhgren describes in his book how he was admitted to the hospital because of a paralyzing stroke and was made a victim of the personnel's desire for power. "I naturally became a victim when one group wanted to prove that I could eat soup and the other that I could not eat this particular soup." (Åhgren 1986, 12)

Martyr, martyrium and *marter* also mean witness or testimony. The suffering human being can also be seen as a witness or a testimony of her innermost being. When the suffering human being expresses or tells about her suffering, she does so with the expectation of credibility and desires that her suffering will be confirmed. Credibility makes up one aspect of a human being's dignity (See Chapter 11). If we do not confirm a human being's suffering, we question her credibility and make her an innocent victim who, in addition to the actual suffering itself, suffers because her credibility has been questioned. The level of suffering is increased and the human being, in symbolic meaning, goes toward a martyr's death as a victim of arbitrariness.

The Patient – The Suffering Human Being

"It is the lot of the human being to be subjected to suffering in all stages of life."

Rousseau 1978, 20

The concept *patient* originally meant the one who suffers, the one who patiently accepts and endures something. The Swedish word *patient* comes from the Latin *patiens*, which means suffering, the root term of which is *pati*, meaning endure, suffer. From *pati* is also derived the Swedish *passiv* and *passion* via the Latin *passio*. The essential meaning of *passio* was suffering, but it later came to mean passion because of the influence of the unrelated Greek term *pathos*. The original meaning of *pathos* is also suffering, but it has received the meaning of passion from stoical philosophy for which the emotions, or passions, were the suffering that disturbed the soul's equilibrium.

In the SAOB Archives there emerges a varied picture of the suffering human being, the patient, as well as how the concept has developed. I shall give here a few examples of the development of the concept during the past centuries. As early as the 18th century one characterized patient types with the help of a prefix. For example, in SAOB we find the following designations:

> A Pox patient (1757); Criminal patient (1894); Heart patient (1886, 1902); Nerve patient (1898); Sea-sick patient (1899); Scoliosis patient (1902); Criminal patient with reference to mental illness (1908).

In spite of the fact that one looked at suffering as a form of illness, one conceived of illness as a relatively broad concept. This emerges in the following expressions:

> "One sought the military doctor…The patient learned that he suffered from an obsession." (1927)

> "Patient, see sick" (1847)

> "who is an eternal patient both in body and soul." (1798)

> "…one illness helps the patient to conquer another." (1926)

> "Patient, a sick person who suffers." (1716)

The concept of patient has, however, not only been limited to illness but even has had a more comprehensive and nuanced meaning, which is given expression in the following:

> "Grandmother who has never been sick, is a troublesome and impatient patient." (1927)

> "Mr. Skytte with his active nature had soon tired of playing patient." (1857, 1866)

> "Nevertheless, one must be governed by the patient's tastes, so long as it is not derived from fretting..." (1717).

There are also expressions for the way one may relate to the patient:

> For that reason, we must let our Lord Jesus Christ so deal with us as a good physician deals with his patient. (1648)

> "Then, go and hang yourself," as the doctor said when the patient complained that she could not walk, stand, or lie down. (1876)

As indicated earlier, it is interesting to note that the concept *patient* did not originally refer to illness. The patient was a person who suffered, had to endure something, was passive and could be patient, but who also had passions, sufferings, and desires. The concept formerly was more clearly associated with all dimensions of human life.

Later the concept of patient passed through a transformation and a reduction. More and more it was given the meaning of one who is ill, has a diagnosis or an infirmity and who is receiving care. The concept of patient thus developed a medical meaning and was related to a specific diagnosis, and consequently the "person who suffers" was largely forgotten. In the SAOB Archives there is some support for this:

> *Patient* means essentially a person who suffers, or in other words, an ill person. It is unnecessary when we have the word *ill* and it is only used for the purpose of avoiding tautology. (1847)

> *Patient*, a sick person who suffers. (1716)

The concept of patient in recent years has also been given the connotation of a social-political or administrative concept by being linked to the official right to receive care and get financial support for treatment. What remains of the original concept is now connected to *passio*, a person who must wait patiently. Paradoxically enough, one can link today's care with the fact that a system that originally was intended to give care to the suffering human being, in many instances causes suffering. To be a patient today one has to give evidence of objective and socially acceptable symptoms for a named ailment, which can be treated and which doesn't cost too much. The concept *patient* in many situations has been replaced with the concepts of *client* or *customer*. In ancient Rome a client was a person who stood under the protection of another, often a more powerful person. A customer is a person who regularly visits a certain business. (Dalin, 1975) Both client and customer have another meaning than patient, especially in relation to suffering.

The concept of patient has both an objective and subjective dimension. The position of the patient is partly based on external objective criteria and partly on the person's subjective experience of illness or suffering.

A humanistically-based science should build on the original concept of the patient as the suffering human being (See Chapter 12). The suffering that we meet in today's health care has many different faces. Although suffering has disappeared as a concept, it has in no way disappeared as a part of human reality. Today we lack a concrete language to express suffering, so the person uses symbols. A symbol can be conceived of as a sign which comprises a derived and often deeper meaning of the phenomenon, in this case, suffering. To understand a patient's suffering, it is important to be sensitive to the symbolic language of people. Despite the fact that suffering in its form of expression has been changed, it is in its deepest essence the same, i.e., a form of dying. Later in this book we shall meet people who are suffering within health care today.

NOTES

[1]The concept analysis discussion in this chapter is based on Eriksson and Herbert's (1993) article "Lidande – en begreppsanalytisk studie" [Suffering – a Concept Analysis Study] in Eriksson (ed.) 1993. The reader who wishes to become more familiar with concept analysis is referred to that article and the work of Koort (1975). In this chapter the Swedish concepts of *lidande* (suffering), *att lida* (to suffer), and the opposite of suffering, *lust* (desire) are examined, based on the Koort method (1975), semantic origin and evolution, and an analysis of their lexical meaning. The analysis used dictionaries from 1850 to 1988 including the *Svenska Akademins Ordbok* (SAOB, the Swedish Academy Dictionary.) The scientific approach is qualitative as well as quantitative.

[2] Topor (1992) calls attention to, among other things, that a person's psychological suffering is changed within psychiatric care into illnesses, which one tries to cure. One forgets the suffering person. The same train of thought is presented by Cassell (1991) when he argues for a new humanistic science-directed medical paradigm where the starting point shall be the person who suffers, and not the illness.

[3] The Icelandic *lida* is used in the same way. The old high German *lidan* and middle-low German *liden* mean experience, live through, and endure (compare with the German *leiden*).

Within the Latin language there are several words for suffering. The word *patientia* has the meaning of the ability to endure or bear. *Passio* means suffering, emotion, or passion. *Dolor* means bodily pain; in part inner pain, torment, and agony; in part melancholy expression or degeneration, movement and pathos.

In New Testament Greek *páscho* means suffer, endure, or tolerate. It comes from *pathos*, suffering. Additional derivations from this word are *pathéma*, suffering, pain, or worry; *pathetos*, emotions, suffering; *kakapatheia*, suffering; *kakapatheo*, suffer or have difficulties; *sympatheo*, compassion or sympathy. Even other words with allusion to suffering are used in the New Testament (*Studiebibeln* 1983).

In Hebrew many words are used with meanings referring to some form of suffering. *Mak'ob* means pain, torment, and suffering. *Asak* means oppression, to suffer oppression. *Kasar* is given the meaning to be cut off, be short; *kalam* means to be the object of shame, and *ana* means to be bowed down or oppressed, to bow, to humble oneself, or patiently bear. *Oni* or *ani* means need, accident, or oppression. Rā'ā means suffer an accident, an accident, misery, and comes from the word *ra'a* meaning to be evil or damaging. (*Illustrerat bibellexikon* 1967).

Even in modern languages such as German, English, and French, one can trace the meanings here named, that is, suffering as pain, agony and torment, but even as passion.

[4] The leading sources for the concept analysis are SAOB archive material, *Swedish Etymological Dictionary*, *The Illustrated Bible Lexicon*, *The Study Bible*, *Latin-Swedish Dictionary*, 2 ed., and several other dictionaries.

Chapter Four

Suffering – A Struggle Between Evil and Good

"God and the Evil One struggle in vain for her soul."

von Wright

Suffering is a struggle between evil and good, between suffering and desire. A common conception is that suffering belongs together with evil. Suffering is generally seen as the working of something evil. As the concept analysis revealed, suffering is the opposite of desire. In desire there is movement, striving and craving after the good, but desire can also be used in the struggle against evil. To suffer always involves a struggle.[1] The person has feelings of fear, anxiety, and agitation in the face of suffering. Suffering is not the same as anxiety; however, a person who suffers can experience anxiety. Anxiety also can be a cause of suffering. When a person experiences anxiety, it is an indeterminate and diffuse feeling that can be intensified to something intolerable. In the moment the person "defines" her anxiety, that is, gives it a definite attribute, she simultaneously is able enter her suffering.

Now the struggle begins. The first step toward overcoming unrest and anxiety is to reshape them into suffering. The problem is that we call unrest and anxiety "suffering" and try to eliminate these feelings instead of reshaping them and providing an opportunity for suffering and struggle. Suffering lies beyond unrest and anxiety. In suffering there is a certainty that we must struggle or give up. Depending on the life situation, one enters the struggle or gives up. In the moment that we cease to struggle, we no longer experience suffering. When the struggle of suffering is most intense, a person often lacks the ability to communicate her suffering to another person.

The struggle against suffering is a life struggle. Von Hartman formulates it in the following words cited in Ljunglund (1914,16):

> As soon as life gets a little breathing space in its struggle, it breaks out into beauty and a display of color among plants and animals; even those who live deep on the bottom of the sea, where no one appreciates all the radiance of beauty. Even the life struggle itself has an aesthetic value.

The struggle of suffering is a type of torment in which the person fights against the feelings of shame and humiliation (compare Lazare 1992). As long as there is movement in the suffering there is hope. Hope consists in a movement toward desire and a sense of meaning in suffering and life.

In the struggle of suffering four basic positions emerge. (Figure 2)[2]

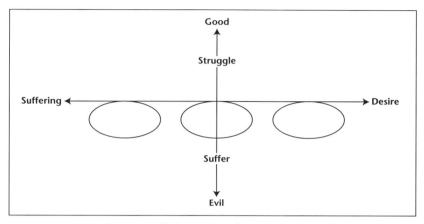

Figure 2. Suffering as Struggle – A Position Model

In good suffering the person is in a struggle for meaning and growth toward a higher degree of integration in order to be a whole person. It is certainty beyond unrest and fear that makes a person strong. Paradoxically, now she can experience desire and feel joy in suffering.[3] In good desire there is genuine joy in life, meaning and strength. In desire that is evil, the person is captive to her passion and is unable to decide about her life; rather, she is driven. Evil suffering is evil throughout and the person often experiences this situation as hopeless. Depending on the different positions and on the person's actual life situation and life view, suffering takes different forms. But suffering is always a unique blending of desire and suffering, good and evil. Each separate suffering has its unique form.

The symbolic forms that guide a person's life consist of *being, will* and *consciousness*. Through these forms, there develops a self-consciousness in the person, that is to say, an insight into one's own suffering. Suffering as a struggle implies the willingness to *be* in suffering and to dare to admit that it exists. The suffering struggle of Jesus is a struggle that mirrors the depth of the suffering between evil and good.

Jung (1993) positions suffering and desire opposite one another and argues that there can be no happiness without suffering. He refers to Schopenhauer who says that happiness is just the end of suffering. Jung argues that suffering and happiness presuppose one another and they are so close to one another that suffering is easily transformed into happiness. Intensive suffering can produce a form of superhuman happiness.

Suffering involves a struggle of the *will*. Such a struggle lies in the nature of life. There are many explanations for the cloven will of people. Von Wright (1987, 64) has expressed it in this way: "The human being is a cloven being. God and the Evil One struggle in vain for her soul."

Ljunglund thinks that the will is a Janus being who turns or should turn one face toward the world of inanimate matter and the other toward the world of life. It is these forms of existence which constitute the object of our volition. Life and matter move in opposite directions and function according to different laws. Life follows the law of freedom whereas matter follows the law of necessity.

> Matter is in itself unchangeable and permits only the shuffling of the already given; the character of life is to grow beyond the frame of the given, a growth which we call "development." (Ljunglund 1914, 26)

To sin against one's own will is presumably something many people know about. When the person sins against her will, she does herself harm and makes herself "unfree." She becomes, as Kierkegaard maintains, pursued by the anguish of sin. "It is a rather peculiar harassment when a person in the strictest sense sins against her own will, pursued by the anguish of sin…" (Kierkegaard 1928, 321). How shall we understand this struggle of the human will that Paul expresses in the words: "For I do not do the good I want, but the evil I do not want is what I do." Romans 7:19.

The human struggle is also a struggle for freedom, a freedom from evil and for the good. The lack of freedom in human beings constitutes one of the grounds for suffering. The struggle for freedom is a struggle between guilt and responsibility. Guilt binds the human being, while the genuine consciousness of responsibility as a human being liberates. Not to assume responsibility involves an experience of guilt. Many seek to evade this responsibility by arguing it away or explaining suffering, but at the deepest level the human being seeks freedom by taking responsibility, a responsibility for oneself and for the other.

Kierkegaard (1928) discusses the freedom of our thoughts and how our thoughts can bind us to evil. He asks the question if people are not responsible for their thoughts. Suffering can lead to a guilt that makes the person anxious and afraid, and causes her to flee to the evil. Through this she can come under the control of evil thoughts. The more anxious the person becomes, the more her evil thoughts have power over her.

Awareness of freedom is one form of the *consciousness* of suffering. "The most painful suffering for a free being is in this way to be unfree in another being's control." (Kierkegaard 1928, 323). Our freedom and the integrity of our being develops from what Bergson (1912) calls our being's interlacing of divergent tendencies.

Ljunglund (1914) feels that we become free through forging our being into a true self that can give us a determination not dependent on or controlled by motives. Such an affirmation of life can happen rapidly or develop slowly. If it happens rapidly, it is seldom without having been preceded by a thorough-going crisis (compare Jesus' 40 days in the wilderness). The person's awareness has been deepened and she has developed a capacity for compassion at the same time as she is aware of her own suffering.

Åkerberg (1987) talks about the idea of the "double suffering aspect." The initial assumption is that life is always a struggle. If the human being is not to be destroyed by the struggle, she must find weapons to counteract the struggle. A one-sided aspect means that human beings have an existential need to place expected or directly experienced unpleasantness of different kinds behind them. The futuristic way of looking at things, to hurry forward in order to get away from suffering, awakens in many the thought of death as the ultimate liberator. The human being seeks to flee from the suffering of the original situation and looks forward to something better at the same time as she shortens the measurable time toward the even greater suffering, the moment of death. When the question of the meaning of life arises in this perspective, in the experience of being "shut out," one can say that the life of the person is in the double suffering model, a struggle between daring to desire and/or to renounce life.

The ability to desire something is obviously in the service of life since its aim is to maintain life. But in the same moment that the desire is moved in the direction of the material and out of balance it forms a covenant with the enemy of life, i.e., material necessities and evil, and the person easily becomes the victim of a variety of earthly temptations.

We must certainly recognize ourselves in the struggle. By daring to follow a course that grows out from our inner self and abiding by that course we have the basis or the direction for our existence. In Greek thought virtue fulfills this function. Faith is also a source, a faith that is partly confidence in ourselves, a faith in life, and a faith that gives life in its entirety a meaning.

NOTES

[1] Suffering as a struggle between good and evil can be derived from the semantic analysis of the concepts *suffering* and *suffer* (cf. Eriksson and Herberts in Eriksson (Ed.) 1993, *Encounters With Suffering* and the empirical material which has emerged in the studies alluded to earlier in Lindholm and Eriksson (1993, a,b.)

[2] The struggle of suffering. We have been able to find support for the various positions in our empirical studies. See Lindholm and Eriksson's discussion of suffering. (ibid.)

[3] There is a power and joy in suffering that is given expression in the literature as well as in the empirical material. In the Bible we find many expressions of joy in suffering.

> I am now rejoicing in my sufferings for your sake, and in my flesh I am completing what is lacking in Christ's afflictions for the sake of his body, that is, the church. Col. 1:24

> ...I am filled with consolation; I am overjoyed in all our affliction. 2 Cor. 7:4

> But rejoice insofar as you are sharing Christ's sufferings... I Peter 4:13

Benktson (1976, 2) states, "Suffering and joy are inextricably joined with one another. All borderline situations are related to suffering. All also release energy." It is precisely suffering in the borderline situations that can be likened to "natural suffering." Fright and fear before the new often creates a feeling of panic among people.

Chapter Five

The *Why* of Suffering

In the moment we stop raising the question "why?" we have had the first victory over our suffering, and we have the freedom to decide what we want to do about it.

Human beings have always had a need to try to explain the world they inhabit and the events of which they are a part. Our picture of the world is formed by faith, knowledge, and superstition. What human beings cannot explain or understand, they often refer to as an external power, fate, or something evil or good. In the deepest sense the question, *why suffering?* is an existential or religious question.

Everyone who is a victim of suffering positions themselves in some phase of the question, *why?* Sometimes we are given an answer, but just as often, it is not given. When people find themselves most deeply involved in the struggle of suffering, they are often beyond the question and find themselves in a suffering that just *is*. The question of the *why* of suffering seems meaningless and remote. In the moment that we cease to ask the question, *why?* we have won our first battle and are free to "endure" the inevitable. Some of the ontology of suffering, its true essence, is found beyond the question, *why?* When people no longer find it necessary to ask, *why?* they have recovered their dignity. The paradoxical truth is that they then often have become more lonely in their suffering.

It is just the question, *why?* which hinders human beings from completing their suffering. Many times it is people in the surroundings of the sufferer who ask the question and perhaps force the sufferer to give too prompt an answer. By trying to find too technical an explanation, we believe that we do something for the sufferer, but in actuality the opposite is true.

We nevertheless return constantly to the question of why suffering exists. The attempt to answer the question shifts among different perspectives and starting points. Some strive to eliminate suffering, others to alleviate it, still others to find its meaning.

Views on the *why* of suffering vary among different sciences and religions. In the Old Testament's story of the Fall, suffering and death are seen as a consequence of the Fall and separation from God. Suffering is a consequence of human sin. The Book of Job is one of the oldest books devoted to suffering and it has been the starting point for innumerable analyses and interpretations of suffering. One of the best known is Jung's answer to Job (Jung 1954). The effort has been made to find a rational interpretation for Job's suffering. Job triumphs over his suffering and regains his good fortune, and this is based on the fact that Job's unfailing faith in the Almighty God never wavers (Hjelm 1960).

The view of suffering in the New Testament is impacted by the sufferings of Christ. He went voluntarily into His suffering. In the New Testament we are shown how Jesus Himself encountered suffering and how He tried to alleviate it among people. It is a living portrait of how love can triumph over suffering. Through faith the person participates in the sufferings of Jesus and becomes aware of the atonement. Through her own act of love for her neighbor she represents the work of reconciliation (see *Illustrated Bible Lexicon*, 1967).

Schopenhauer (1905), "the philosopher of suffering," proceeded from the premise that life was a single long process of suffering. His answer to the question of why suffering exists is that the only route of escape is to deny the will to live.

Quite independent of how we answer the question about the *why* of suffering, it is important that at some phase of our life we raise it. We are then forced to reflect and to make ourselves responsible for an answer. We should try to find an answer that makes it possible for us to penetrate the question of suffering more deeply and to learn to understand suffering even more.

To Live Is To Suffer

To truly live is to dare to choose suffering.

To suffer can sometimes involve the choice of how we want to live our life. Suffering, as we have already indicated, is a part of life. But all human beings do not have the possibility to choose, and as we have already indicated, there are many who lack the ability to suffer. Many have been distanced from natural suffering, i.e., the suffering that is a part of a person's natural growth and development. Karin Boye (1935, 38) formulates it in this manner, "Of course it hurts when the buds burst. Otherwise why would spring hesitate?"

Suffering is related to the levels on which one lives. For the person whose primary relationship is social, suffering can be the exclusion from friendship or not to experience that one has a place in life. For the person who strives for freedom or to satisfy her own needs and be allowed to be who she wants to be, suffering can consist of loneliness where she experiences that she is not understood and that no one can give her what she needs.

In its deepest meaning suffering can imply that the person is unable to be shaped in accordance with what she is intended for so that she cannot actualize her innermost being. The deepest suffering implies that life energy is lost and the person is filled with depression.

Each person at some time confronts a suffering that is unendurable. In her suffering the person is always in some respect alone. In suffering a person stands before something which at the moment feels like an inescapable fate. This something can be almost anything. Suffering has no given determinant. Each suffering is unique and may be seen as the solitary's encounter with the solitary. In the deepest suffering a human being stands before something we can call the "wall of suffering," something that seems impenetrable but where a gleam of light penetrates the darkness.

People express their suffering in several ways, but often we lack a language to express what we really experience. We are forced to transform our suffering to a shape we can describe in a more tangible way. We are forced to give our suffering an explanation. Our suffering is transformed to pain, anxiety or a physical expression that can be observed. Our human suffering is reduced to something the surrounding world finds an acceptable and manageable phenomenon.

There is also a suffering we could call *relation-less*—a suffering the person carries within and which has been caused by a feeling of insufficiency, self-condemnation, and inability to live the life she would wish to live.

To Cause Suffering For The Other

Only the human being who denies suffering can cause suffering.

It is most frequently human beings who cause another's suffering. There is, to be sure, a suffering caused by natural catastrophes, and situations for which human beings apparently cannot be responsible. But such sufferings one can understand in some way with a sensible explanation since they are tangible. The suffering we human beings cause one another is frequently concealed. Sometimes this happens quite unconsciously. Buber (1989) writes that no human being can do evil wholeheartedly. It is only the good that one can do whole-heartedly.

Why then does the human being get into a situation where she does the evil she does not want to do, but the good she wants to do she fails to do? The fundamental question is whether we truly want to do the good. Evil and good are related to one's freedom. Freedom means at the deepest level to be responsible. To be responsible for someone else implies that we do not cause them suffering. A human being who has suffered and has experienced suffering and has been reconciled to her suffering has difficulty consciously causing suffering for another. The suffering that human beings cause one another has its basis in human relationships. The lack of any meaningful relationship constitutes perhaps the greatest suffering.

To cause suffering for the other always implies violation of the dignity of the other, failure to confirm this human being's full worth. It is to fail to recognize the human being as potentially holy. To cause suffering for the other is simultaneously to violate one's own dignity and to deny one's own holiness.

If we seek an explanation for the suffering we consciously or unconsciously cause one another, we must examine our view of reality, our world view and the basis of our values. The history of suffering belongs together with the history of compassion and the responsibility we are prepared to assume for each other.

The Christian Interpretation

"All suffering comes from my love for that which adversity has taken from me."

Meister Eckhart

There are many people who when confronted with the *why* of suffering, turn to God. Where sickness and suffering exist, questions emerge of sin, guilt and punishment, and these questions are thought by many to be religious. One asks if suffering is God's punishment and if one has been disobedient towards God. Since this question seems to be so central among people, I will deal with it briefly.[1]

Within the biblical perspective suffering is connected with the problem of evil. For this there is no comprehensive unified interpretation or acceptable explanation. A number of solutions for the problem of suffering have been advanced for the purpose of assisting the Christian person to understand why she is stricken by suffering.[2]

Stott[3] differentiates between "natural" evil and "moral" evil. He associates natural evil with suffering and the moral evil with sin. He looks at human suffering from the perspective of the cross of Christ. Seiler (1989) feels that Christ's death on the cross is God's lowering himself into the ultimate loneliness. In death is the greatest threat to human existence—to be shut out from nearness, communion, and love. To be alone is that which most contradicts our being as humans.

When it comes to the question of sin, Stott (1986) believes that suffering may be caused by the sin of others. Examples are when a child suffers at the hands of loveless or irresponsible parents or when people starve because of economic injustice.

Lindblom[4] (1940, 158) feels that if suffering is of necessity connected with the individual's sin, the problem of suffering is incapable of solution. The aims of suffering must be broadened, and in order to find a solution we must make clear for ourselves that there is suffering which can serve entirely different purposes than those advanced in the Old Testament and Hellenistic perspective. According to this perspective, suffering is seen as a punishment for human transgression. Lindblom feels that it is un-Christian to ask a suffering person what that person has done. It is Christian to try to find meaning in suffering and see it as positive energy and to bear one's own suffering in order that through this, God will be glorified and the suffering person be seen as a testimony to God's power in a frail human being.

Stott (1986, 315-329) refers to Jesus' comments on suffering which shall show to people God's glory. God reveals His glory through suffering. Stott refers to six possible answers to the question of how the cross can speak to people in their suffering:

1. The cross of Christ is *a stimulus to patient endurance*. Even though suffering has to be recognized as evil and therefore resisted, there nevertheless comes a time when it has to be realistically accepted.

2. The cross of Christ is *the path to mature holiness*...Just as suffering led to maturity through obedience for Christ, so it leads to maturity through perseverance for us...if God's love is holy love, as it is, then it is concerned not only to act in holiness (as in the cross of Christ), but also to promote holiness (in the people of God).

3. The cross of Christ is *the symbol of suffering service*...It is not just that suffering belongs to service, but that suffering is indispensable to fruitful or effective service.

4. The cross of Christ is *the hope of final glory*...As [people] share in his sufferings, they would also share in his glory...It is, then, the hope of glory which makes suffering bearable.

5. The cross of Christ is *the ground of a reasonable faith*. All suffering, physical and emotional, sorely tries our faith...Job has been

invited to look afresh at the creation, and has glimpsed the glory of the Creator...What God gave Job was a comprehensive introduction to the wonders of nature, and thereby a revelation of his creative genius, which silenced Job's accusations and led him...to humble himself, repent of his rebellion, and trust God again.

6. The cross of Christ is *the proof for God's solidary love*, that is, of his personal, loving solidarity with us in our pain. For the real sting of suffering is not misfortune itself, nor even the pain of it or the injustice of it, but the apparent God-forsakenness of it. Pain is endurable, but the seeming indifference of God is not.

It is interesting to note how the Christian interpretation of death, loneliness, communion and love relate to human descriptions of suffering. The Christian interpretation provides the basis for an understanding, and what one understands is easier to endure. Jung (1960) emphasizes the importance of understanding suffering and the significance of a philosophical or religious perspective.

Suffering Has No Given Determinant

"Living beings are made to suffer through being born, they live by causing suffering, and they usually die during suffering."   Allport

When we raise the question of why suffering exists, we often look for a cause or explanation of it. Suffering has no given determinant. Almost anything can cause suffering. I shall here describe some of the prominent circumstances that cause suffering. In Chapter 11 we shall return to the question of the suffering of patients.

Dignity and Guilt

Suffering violates a person's dignity and to violate human dignity is to cause suffering. To suffer, basically, is beneath the person. Each time a person suffers she feels violated. This feeling of violation results in a person's hesitance to discuss her suffering, especially when she finds herself in the middle of it. A suffering person is very unhappy; besides this, she feels ashamed about being unhappy. A person suffers because of guilt, but at the same time she may want to suffer in order to atone for her guilt (Frankl 1974). There is a connection between suffering and guilt. All persons carry guilt because of various faults, large or small, for which in some way they feel responsible. The experience of guilt becomes a suffering the moment that the person becomes conscious of failing herself. A full consciousness of guilt occurs often after the act. When a person sins, she is conscious of the evil she does in the execution of the act. The feeling of guilt is a form of suffering and she wants to expiate her guilt or in some way pay for it. The atonement doctrine of the Old Testament includes the idea of a sacrificial offering. A person is atoned for through making a sacrifice. Through suffering the person can expiate her guilt. This has sometimes led to a search for suffering in order to expiate one's guilt. Siegel (1990) emphasizes the significance of a person's ability to forgive herself. If a person lacks self-esteem and cannot forgive herself, illness can be the atonement that frees her from her guilt.

To try to see meaning in one's own suffering and to find an answer to the question *why?* is a way for a person to confirm self-worth. To encounter a suffering person and to try to share her suffering presupposes the greatest sensitivity. A suffering person needs to get confirmation of her worth as a human being.

To suffer implies not being a whole and complete person. It is a part of human nature for a person to satisfy, as long as possible, her most primary needs and desires. When this is no longer possible, it is the person's right to secure help from someone in her immediate surroundings, someone who sees her needs and desires and intervenes without her having to ask for help. To be forced to ask for help for the most basic needs, to experience that no one sees or understands what one needs, not to experience one's full worth as a human being, is suffering.

Condemnation

"...If anyone of you is without sin, let him be the first to throw a stone at her." John 8:7

Many people today experience condemnation on different levels. One condemns oneself and one experiences the condemnation of God and others. By condemning another and acting as a judge of the other we cause much suffering. How quick are we to condemn those who are different, those who do not share our thoughts and values? The task of a human being is not to condemn but to understand and to forgive. To condemn is to declare the other invalidated and to obliterate her as a human being. We have the right to declare separate acts invalid, but not human beings. Jesus' word to the woman was, "Go and sin no more."

In these words we find love. Condemnation is to the contrary loveless and in all respects, evil.

Lack of Love

Deprive me rather of life than the capacity to love.

A human being's deepest desire is the desire for love and confirmation. To not receive and to not be able to give love involves a limitless suffering. A human being's dignity is confirmed by the mediation of love. Lack of love hinders us from feeling compassion and from entering a deep relationship with another person. Both professional literature and fiction are filled with descriptions of how lack of love causes suffering.

To Not Be Taken Seriously

Dear God, at least let me be a good clown.

The experience of not being taken seriously, to experience that no one reckons with me, can cause unendurable suffering. It can give us a feeling that we do not exist for others. It is a hopeless situation since every effort to make contact is meaningless. To not be taken seriously is to be questioned about one's identity and to be deprived of all possibilities to affirm one's own identify. In order to protect oneself from unendurable suffering a person may put on a clown's mask. Then the person can act out her suffering with the help of the tragic element in the comedian's dress. In spite of everything, it is better to be a clown than to be nobody.

Loneliness

"My soul finds no rest until it can rest in God." Augustine

The aloneness that implies being excluded from all communion can involve serious suffering, yet all aloneness is by no means suffering. Aloneness becomes suffering when a person is too alone in her aloneness. Not to be allowed to be alone or have privacy can also involve suffering. There are people who live in life's most intense turmoil, in the midst of other people, who nevertheless experience a deep loneliness. There are people who live totally alone who do not feel lonely or deserted. They have communion with existence itself. Why do so many experience aloneness as suffering and others almost long for solitude? There is an intolerable loneliness where a person feels that she is deprived of something she once had as her own or that she would wish to have as her own. It is the loneliness that is experienced as a form of "dying" which becomes suffering.

To Be Not Welcome

"...there was no place for them in the inn."   Luke 2:7

The experience of not being welcome when one comes honestly filled with expectation produces suffering. All human beings want to experience that they are invited[5] and welcome to a communion, that someone waits for them and longs for them. To feel not welcome, regardless if the situation is an individual, concrete one or if it is life in its entirety, deprives the person of hope and the joy of living. To welcome someone means to show respect, to confirm the other.

All the described experiences that can cause suffering seem to have a common denominator: it always involves a violation of human dignity when something is experienced as suffering. A person can endure loneliness, lack of love, guilt, etc., as long as it does not violate her as a human being. This argument leads to a supposition that there is only one answer to the question of the *why* of suffering. Suffering can be experienced as different conditions, feelings and situations, but at the deepest level suffering is caused by deprivation of a human being's dignity in its objective and/or subjective meaning.

NOTES

[1] The presentation makes no claim of being complete or exhaustive. That would presuppose a thorough theological discussion, which is beyond the objective of this book and my own area of competence. I want only to present a few ideas emerging from patients' questions.

[2] See, for example, Stott (1986, 273) and Stanley (1934). Stott feels that the Bible does not strive to explain the origin of suffering. Rather, it strives to help us bear it.

[3] Stott (1986, 273-274) tries to come further than what he calls usual, standard arguments about suffering being an intrusion into God's fair world, and being the result of sin.

[4] Lindblom (1940, 157-158) in his book *The Book About Job and His Suffering* has given a penetrating analysis of the suffering of Job. He seeks answers for the riddle of suffering and illuminates the question from a literary and religious perspective. He provides different ways to interpret suffering from Old and New Testament perspectives.

1. Suffering as a means of testing, teaching, and tempering. This point of view is found in the Old Testament as well as in ancient Greece and the New Testament. In Paul's letter to the Romans (Romans 5:3,4) we find, "...we also boast in our sufferings, knowing that suffering produces endurance, and endurance produces character, and character produces hope."

2. Suffering as chastisement for sin (here Lindblom is talking about external suffering). This point of view is found also in the New Testament where Paul in I Corinthians presents the view that many have become sick and even died because of an unworthy use of the Lord's Supper. Such punishment can be a healthful warning. In the New Testament the rule also applies, "What a person sows she will also reap." And Paul writes to the Romans, "Sin can conceive new sin."

3. Parallelism. The person as a "Christ person" is someone who in all respects must be an image of Christ and in the entire life process be like Him. To suffer is an act of righteousness.

4. Suffering on earth will be compensated. There is a conception that suffering on earth will be compensated in another existence, beyond the grave. Paul says in Romans 8:18, "I consider that the sufferings of this present time are not worth comparing with the glory about to be revealed to us."

5. Suffering is an essential element in God's self-revelation and can serve to glorify God.

6. Suffering is a means for the revelation of God's love in its unfathomable depths. Reference is here made to John 3:16, "For God so loved the world that He gave His only Son, so that everyone who believes in Him may not perish but may have eternal life."

[5] Kierkegaard (1939) has emphasized the word "invitation" and discusses it in detail in his book *Practical Christianity*.

Chapter Six

The Meaning of Suffering

Only love can give meaning to suffering, because the greatest of all is love.

The question of the meaning of suffering is perhaps the most diffi-cult to grasp. In the literature we note an ambivalent attitude toward the question. One desires in some way to find the meaning of suffering. "A meaning of suffering is determined by how it is encountered", says Topor (1992, 80) and this is applicable at least in the area of psychiatry.

Frankl[1] starts from the premise that there is meaning in suffering. Each person has her own specific calling and mission in life, a concrete task that must be completed. Every person's mission is unique as well as her special possibility to complete this mission. Each time a person is confronted by an inescapable situation, she has the possibility of actual-izing the highest value, to fulfill the deepest meaning—the meaning of suffering.

The most significant thing is our attitude toward suffering. When one no longer can heal or alleviate another's suffering, one should try to mobilize that person's ability to fulfill the meaning of the suffering. A common notion is that suffering in itself has no meaning but that it can be assigned a meaning through being connected with something else. One view about the meaning of suffering is that it is the true source of meaning in life. When a person has discovered this source, suffering disappears or at least gives the person some options—to continue this suffering or to integrate the newly achieved insight and to cease to suffer (cf. Topor 1992).

The thought that a person would consciously choose to suffer feels somewhat strange, and we have found no support for this conclusion in the investigations we have carried out. The discovery of the source of suffering certainly can lead to an experience of meaning when one has passed through the suffering and can look back. For some, time is needed to integrate the newly discovered insight, which in no way implies the desire to continue the suffering.

The meaning in suffering emerges when a person reconciles herself with the situation and thereby finds possibilities and meaning. The expe-rience of suffering seems bound to an experience of different possibili-ties in the actual life situation. Kierkegaard (1928) sees the category of possibility as the deepest of all categories. Suffering can be transformed to desire and joy by the help of an insight of new, unsuspected possibili-ties. It is a gleam of hope that enters a situation that previously seemed hopeless. Movement away from passivity in suffering seems to go in two directions—through the creative leap or through subordination and reconciliation.

Suffering receives its meaning when the person by passing through an inescapable suffering receives the possibility of actualizing her innermost being. Frankl (1990, 132) speaks of three ways to find meaning: creative values, experiential values, and attitudinal values. Creative values are actualized in actions; experiential values are actualized by experiencing the world; and attitudinal values, when one chooses her attitude toward suffering and unchangeable or inescapable fate. If the person cannot change circumstances, she must change her attitudes toward the circumstances. The change can provide a new insight about circumstances despite the fact that they cannot be changed. Faith, hope, and love can alter our attitude in spite of the fact that the concrete circumstances have not been changed.

There is a threat to suffering and in a person's ability to grow in it. The threat lies in not seeing the suffering and its possibilities or to see it and to seek to eliminate it or to explain it away without making it a part of life. This should not be interpreted as an effort to beautify suffering or not to see the evil in it.

If we deny suffering, we deny a part of life and the possibility of a person's becoming a whole human being. The art of confronting suffering lies in confirming the good while at the same time denying and rejecting evil. Indifference is a threat to suffering. To be indifferent implies lacking the energy to perceive, lacking the energy to see, or hear, or receive. Indifference is the lack of movement, of pleasure, of hope, of desire, of longing. This lack is also a form of suffering. One can ask if the key to the riddle of suffering is in the movement between suffering and desire, or in the person's ability to love passionately and affirm life in all its glory while at the same time impartially integrating painful and unavoidable suffering.[2] Through a union of extreme opposites, possibilities are created, and suffering can receive meaning. The meaning of suffering exists in that it generates a capacity for compassion and love.[3]

Jung (1993) introduces the thought that suffering has a meaning and a task in relation to life in its entirety, and that suffering helps the person to be aware. However, he realizes that it may be super-human to overcome suffering. On the other hand, to overcome suffering can result in a feeling of happiness and satisfaction.

There is an unnecessary suffering, a suffering that has no meaning whatsoever. We must do all in our power to eliminate unnecessary suffering. Unnecessary suffering is that generated by human evil, the suffering for which we cannot discern any reasonable meaning. Unnecessary suffering must be separated from innocent suffering, the suffering that to us seems meaningless (cf. Hjelm 1960).

The Meaning of Suffering in a Christian Perspective

The meaning of suffering is evident in a Christian perspective. The interpretation, nevertheless, varies among different authors.

The question of the meaning of suffering is often actualized in various crisis situations such as war, catastrophe, or illness. That this is the case is often described in the literature and we have also found support for it in our research.

Fjellbu (1941, 17) maintains that it is not the sufferings of Jesus that in themselves create meaning, but the attitude Jesus manifested while He suffered and through His suffering won a victory for suffering humankind. Fjellbu means that the suffering of Jesus was meaningless in itself, but it was given meaning when seen against the background of the fact that He triumphed over suffering. Fjellbu states that "we cannot find the meaning of suffering by explaining suffering but by being given power to deal with suffering and to be witnesses to what the power of Christ can achieve."

Here again we get a picture of the meaning of suffering, not as having a meaning in itself, but something that develops in relation to suffering and gives us the strength to move on. Suffering in itself has no power; it must be combined with something else if power is to be mobilized. Fjellbu uses the story of the man born blind to illustrate the meaning of Jesus' acts. The man was not blind because of the misdeeds of his parents but because this condition allowed a manifestation of God's acts. Evil cannot always be conquered by being explained, but because we do God's acts.

The meaning of suffering is concerned with our love for God: "We know that all things work together for good for those who love God..." (Rom. 8:28). It is rather demanding to comprehend these words and to admit that one has found meaning in one's suffering. Fjellbu means that only through the love for God can suffering be given meaning. This implies, consequently, that we suffer for someone or something else.

In all the different descriptions of the meaning of suffering, we arrive at what Frankl means, that there is an "in order to" which gives suffering its meaning. There is nothing in the causes of suffering or in suffering itself that gives it meaning, but it is this "in order to." Suffering receives meaning when, in some respect, you suffer for something or for someone else, when you can actualize the person's highest task, to be for or to be in God's service for someone else.

NOTES

[1] Viktor Frankl belongs to those one readily thinks about when approaching the question of the meaning of suffering. Frankl sees suffering as a watchman—a protection. Suffering will protect us from apathy, from psychic *rigor mortis*. In suffering we mature, we grow and it may make us richer and stronger. Illness gives a person the possibility of suffering, but we must be aware of the fact that a person can be ill without suffering. There is even a suffering beyond all illness, i.e., the fundamental human suffering that is related to the absence of meaning in existence (Frankl 1990, 134-137).

The question about the meaning of suffering is constantly relevant. Kallenberg (1992) has edited a book, *The Meaning of Suffering*, which illuminates this question from many perspectives. The authors feel that suffering above all constitutes the practical and moral problem to which we must relate in our own lives.

Suffering is a part of what Frankl calls "the tragic triad of human existence." Frankl says , "This three-leaf clover consists of pain, guilt, and death. There is no human being who can say that she has not failed, or suffered, or shall not die." (Frankl 1986).

[2] According to Rollo May (1972) pain and suffering make a human being more sensitive. When we run away from pain, we lose our vitality, our ability to feel and even to love. "To love means to open oneself to both the negative and positive, to grief and to despair and disappointment as well as to joy, perfection, and an awareness so intense that we did not know that such a thing was possible."

We now face one of the deepest and most meaningful paradoxes. It is the fact that our awareness of death gives us a more intense openness towards love while at the same time loves brings with it an increased sense of death.

[3] Brantschen (1988, 58-59) means that love and suffering belong together. The person who cannot suffer cannot love either.

[4] Fjellbu (1941, 17). Fjellbu's ideas were presented initially in a radio address on Norwegian radio in 1940 before the invasion of Norway.

Chapter Seven

The Drama of Suffering

*Within every human being there is
a deep longing that she will be
allowed to play the drama
of her life's suffering.*

There is a suffering in caring created by the expectations experienced when one enters a human encounter or a caring relationship. We have called this "the drama of suffering."[1] It is a drama because it is filled with expectations that have been newly awakened after they have perhaps been belittled time and again.

Every person's suffering is played out in a drama of suffering. To try to alleviate the suffering of a fellow human being involves daring to be a fellow actor in the drama. Every person steps into the drama in the form she desires most of all to take on, in the innermost being of her suffering. If she does not find a fellow actor, she is forced time and again to change her guise until she finds one. It is the naked suffering, the purely physical anguish free from every metaphysical dimension that finally emerges. It is obvious that today a person finds it difficult to give suffering a *gestalt*, and we can ask what accounts for this. In part a person lacks a language that will express her suffering and her innermost feelings. Suffering has often been reduced to the language of illness or physical suffering. To reduce suffering to physical suffering always implies that the person is deprived of the possibilities to alleviate suffering as well as the possibilities for growth, development and reconciliation.

It is a variegated drama that plays out in our encounters with suffering. Many people seem to lack a co-actor in the drama of their suffering. Is it that we have become insensitive to the suffering of others or do we lack the ability to dare to encounter others? Johannisson (1992) insists that not all suffering has legitimacy. Only that which can find room within established social or scientific frameworks can be accepted as a veritable suffering. Sachs (1992) emphasizes that the one who suffers needs a response both concretely and socially. The core of suffering is that which must be communicated through symbols in order to become visible for the surrounding world.

The drama of suffering has three acts:
1. The confirmation of suffering
2. The suffering itself; time and space to undergo the suffering.
3. Reconciliation, i.e., the way to a new wholeness.

To confirm another person's suffering implies conveying to the other, "I see." That another person sees my suffering implies a comfort, an assurance that someone will come to meet me. Confirmation of suffering can happen in a number of ways: a look, a touch, a little word. Not to confirm suffering implies that one overlooks or explains away suffering, which often implies further suffering. To confirm suffering implies that one will not abandon the other, that one is available, gives an *invitation* to the sufferer, and provides time and space to undergo the suffering. To invite the other as *a guest of honor* to an unconditional communion is a way of expressing that one is there to share the struggle of the suffering.

Every person who suffers needs time and space to suffer. We can deprive a person of the possibility to suffer through arguing away or by too rapidly finding reasons for her suffering. To *be* in suffering means to oscillate between suffering and desire and between hope and hopelessness. A person who suffers often prefers being alone despite the fact she wants to experience a feeling of communion. To feel abandoned in her suffering easily creates a feeling of hopelessness, and that, in turn, generates despair. Despair is a condition where hope no longer exists and which leads to death. A despairing person can no longer create new life. A despairing person is prepared to suffer humiliation in order to secure alleviation of her suffering.

Pauli (1930, 95)[2] says, "We suffer humiliation voluntarily and in an action we may manifest our disassociation from the point at issue." In the confessional a person can share that which burdens the conscience with a fellow human being "who is worthy of this confidence." The confessional is a way of expressing one's suffering.

The third act in the drama of suffering, a drama with a happy ending, implies being reconciled.[3] To be reconciled means finding a *new life* and forming a new entity in that life where something has definitely been lost. Reconciliation means to create a new wholeness that includes *the evil* which now is included in a new meaningful wholeness or holiness. A person who has attained reconciliation can often assign a meaning to the experienced suffering. A reconciled person enters a renewed communion with others and experiences a liberation and freedom to *become*. The way of reconciliation can appear to be different for different people. Sometimes reconciliation happens after a humiliating struggle and perhaps deep contrition. Sometimes it happens through a quiet insight into the inescapable realities of existence. But regardless of how the reconciliation occurs, it implies a transformation; a new entity has been created.

If a person cannot play along in the drama of suffering that leads to a true reconciliation, she experiences an intensified suffering, which eventually leads to contrition and a form of dying. The person literally dies, first as a person and a human being in spirit and soul, and little by little, even in body.[4] According to Jung (1941) the person dies before death reaches the body. Death hides itself in the hungry soul. We can flee from our problems, but the flight is death for the soul. We can wear our masks, but they cannot hide our innermost fear.

NOTES

[1] The idea of the drama of suffering originally emerged from the analysis of responses from informants in the research project, "The Home" (See Lindholm and Eriksson 1993, a,b). Johannison (1992, 117) has followed a similar path and maintains that suffering presupposes a co-actor. A suffering person expects to be met by compassion, love, and care.

[2] Ebba Pauli, 1873-1941, was educated in social work and made a major contribution to social care and education in Sweden. In addition to her practical work she carried out a comprehensive social-pedagogic writing career (Dahl, 1949). The encounter with Ebba Pauli, whose most active time as a writer was in the 1930s, has been interesting. In our research about suffering and health we had already established, in our opinion, new concepts such as becoming and the struggle of suffering when I fortuitously came in contact with Ebba Pauli's work.

[3] The concept of reconciliation may seem strange to some. Many see it as a theological concept. The concept could be interchanged with integration, but since this is a more technical term we would like to use reconciliation since this refers to the process of re-creating oneness, a oneness which includes holiness, human dignity.

[3] This is portrayed in Malmberg's poem, *Dårarna*.

Chapter Eight

Compassion —
To Suffer With the Other

"Moral courage is to have compassion."

                    May 1988, 14

To suffer with another, i.e., to experience compassion, is not the same as to suffer oneself. The ability to experience and to express compassion can be hindered by one's own suffering. For example, we have met parents who suffer so much in their children's suffering that they are incapable of compassion. Compassion is the source of all true caring. "So much compassion, so much caring," (Eriksson 1992 b). Compassion presupposes courage, the courage to assume responsibility and the courage of sacrifice something of one's self.

Schopenhauer[1] conceives of compassion as the basic phenomenon of ethics. He believes that the reason for suffering is the tragically blind will to live. If one accepts this maxim, one is freed from the demonic circle of egoism, and experiences the other's tribulation as his own. Compassion becomes the motive for one's actions, while ideas of one's own fortune move into the background replaced by the will to help where help is needed. Compassion is the true principle in every complete justice and every true mercy. Dostoyevsky[2] sees the incapacity for compassion as one of the greatest sins.

The Concept Of Compassion

The concept of compassion constitutes one of the basic concepts of caring science and of caring itself. The thought content of the concept refers to the contextual meaning of caring in which caring is seen as an ethical act in which a person as caregiver has courage to assume responsibility for the other (the patient). The thought content also refers to the fact that the caregiver has courage to sacrifice something of herself for the other. The sacrifice is not made with thought of personal gain but because one truly wants to do something for the other.

On the basis of concept analysis[3], compassion can be interpreted as sensitivity to the pain and suffering of the other. This sensitivity or tenderness prepares us to struggle with the suffering of the other and to try to alleviate it. These are ideas that Schopenhauer's texts also communicate.

Compassion is often associated with mercy.[4] However, with the emergence of humanism, the concepts of compassion and mercy been replaced by concepts such as humanity and goodness and thereby their meaning has been altered.[5]

The concept of compassion has a variegated meaning and is even given a negative meaning, depending in part on the fact that compassion, in a social sense, is connected with other people's needs and wants. For example, wealthy people give of their abundance to the poor. True compassion is thus reduced to a social attitude.

Compassion and mercy were actualized in ancient Greece through various works of mercy or virtues. Compassion is not actually compassion until it has been concretized in action. Sometimes the difference between compassion, the capacity to truly suffer with the other, and the experience of personal suffering is almost non-existent.

The will to save life at any cost and to perform charitable deeds and acts of love unselfishly has been found in people throughout the ages. This will has found different expressions in different time periods and has been dependent on circumstances.

Vonhoff's (1962) description of the history of mercy also constitutes a description of the history of caring. Mercy and true human love, as they were carried out in ancient Egypt, form what I would like to call caritative caring (Eriksson 1990). In ancient Egypt merciful acts were carried out among all who needed help.

> The land of the Nile is constantly shaken by new social unrest, people are made to suffer under bondage to Pharaoh and there is great need and much misery. But one thing is unalterable: here in Egypt people are among the first in word and deed to demand and carry out works of mercy. It is not the "god of war" who gives Egyptian history its most distinctive feature, but the "god of harvest." And there are features that testify to communal order and to maturity, life wisdom and active love for the neighbor. In none of the histories of other peoples do these traits emerge with nearly the same strength. The history of mercy truly begins in the land of the Nile. (Vonhoff 1962, 15)

It is interesting to see that the history of caring follows traits in the history of mercy. Mercy and love for human beings were practiced through the seven physical works of mercy: 1) feed the hungry; 2) give the thirsty drink; 3) clothe the naked; 4) house the stranger; 5) free the captives; 6) care for the sick; and 7) bury the dead. Throughout history, these works of mercy have been present in a number of forms among orders of charity, organizations of benevolence, in diaconal ministries, in health care, and in care of the sick.

Beyond these are spiritual acts of mercy: 1) teach the ignorant; 2) counsel the doubting; 3) warn the sinful; 4) comfort the grieving; 5) forgive those who blaspheme; 6) bear injustice with patience; and

7) pray for the living and the dead (Dahlby 1963).

When one follows the description of the history of mercy and then encounters a loveless world filled with hatred, even though one upholds the principles of humanity and goodness, the question is raised about what constitutes the basic will in a person to do good, be merciful, and to love as the most essential.

Perhaps the clearest expression for human love and mercy within caring is found in Florence Nightingale and her unselfish and pioneering work among the wounded in the midst of the fiery war in Scutari and Crimea.

> With a lamp in her hand she goes through the rooms of pain, holding the hand of the dying, bringing them healing as far as she can and remaining with them until their last breath...Her quiet act gives the sick new hope...With amazement it becomes clear to the suffering that they are still human beings and are treated as human beings... (Vonhoff 1962, 176)

Florence Nightingale even became a model for Henri Dunant, who through a pioneering work founded the Red Cross, and introduced the concept of mercy as a leading and living thought within all its activities. Huber (1946, 173) writes in his description of mercy:

> In the bottomless, clear depths, which are opened to us in the story of the Good Samaritan, the Master shows us a pure and unselfish act. It was performed in a remote and dangerous place; it concerned an absolutely unknown person; there was no thought of any recompense...

This thought of mercy and showing mercy are expressions of the holiness of human beings. It is to show grace and not to condemn. In the act of mercy the person does not ask who is her neighbor. She herself is the neighbor. Compassion is the core of mercy.

NOTES

[1] See Schopenhauer (1905, 86-87) about morality, chapter II.   I am repeating some chosen segments from the Schopenhauer text because it is so expressive:

> Compassion is an undeniable element in the human consciousness; it is one of the identifying signs and does not depend on earlier conceptions, ideas "a priori," religion; dogmas, myths, training or cultivation; it develops spontaneously, immediately, and is unchanging in its nature; it endures in all tests and is to be found in all times and all countries...One appeals to compassion in the assurance of being heard, for one is certain that it is found in all human beings and those ideas are never credited to strange gods...A person who does not feel compassion is beyond all humanity...to be sure, humanity is sometimes synonymous with compassion.

[2] See citation in Wikström (1990, 295).

[3] When we seek for the origin of the concept of the Swedish *medlidande* we are often referred to sympathy. The prefix "sym," from the Greek, has come from "syn", from Atticca "xyn" and is without known connection. Sympathy comes from the Greek *sympatheia* and means compassion. From the Greek word is derived the Latin *compassio*, a translation and from that comes the Swedish *medlidande* (suffering with), the Danish *medlidenhed*, the German *mitleid*, the Icelandic *sampina* and corresponding words in Slavic and other languages.

There exists an interesting derivation of the concept *medlidsam* from the concept *ömhet*. The concept "öm" comes from Old Swedish *ömber* which means "tender," "sensitive," "difficult," "sad," "weak," "miserable," etc. The Icelandic *aumer* means unhappy, miserable, and the Danish *om* means *öm*. The Gotlandic *aumber* has the meaning "evil." A relationship can probably be found with the Greek *aethlos* with the meaning toil, battle, which is related to the Sansrit *vayati* that means wearing oneself out.

The root meaning of the concept "öm" is poor, miserable, unhappy, etc. and from this is derived "sensitive" to pain, smärta, smärtsam. Compare to the South German dialect term *mir ist arm*, = I have pain, feel pain. From this meaning *medlidsam*—essentially sensitive to the pain of others—can be explained. Some, however, believe the meaning to be abstracted from the Icelandic *aumhjartadr* = "tender-hearted," or *ömkan*, that is, pity.

Mercy, compassion, and sympathy have also been replaced by the later concept empathy which in the 1950s came into Swedish from the English. Empathy comes from the Greek *en* = "in" and *patheia*= "suffering," therefore "in suffering." Empathy now appears in contemporary lexicons as "living insight" and a feeling of sympathy. It concerns a psychological identification with the thoughts, feelings, and problems of other people. Empathy is thus a more limited concept than compassion and is thus not synonymous with compassion.

In the *Illustrated Bible Lexicon* (Odeberg & Gilbrant 1967) *medlidande* is given the following meanings:

1. *nud* = to move here and there, be shaken; with the preposition *le* = show someone compassion,

2. *sympatheo* = suffer together with; have sympathy with,

3. *sympathés* = who suffers with another, sympathetic. From this word comes the substantive *sympatheia* = sympathy.

The meaning in the *Illustrated Bible Lexicon* is not unambiguous. It is interesting that in the substantive *sympatheia* something of the original content has been reduced since here the meaning of sympathy is stated.

[4] Synonyms in Swedish for compassion include words such as: *deltagande* - taking part; *medkänsla* - sympathy; *barmhärtighet* – mercy; representing the strongest synonyms. In biblical texts there are references to compassion and mercy. There are references to Jesus' having pity on the outcasts, the lost, the tempted, the sorrowing (Matthew 9:36, Luke 19:41, Heb. 2:18, Luke 22:32, John 11:33,34). There are references to human compassion, and friendship, and believers are challenged to be compassionate (Romans 12:15, Job 2:11 and 30:25, John 11:19).

[5] See Vonhoff (1962) and Eriksson (1990).

Chapter Nine

Suffering and Health

*Suffering can give health a meaning
just as it can rob life of all meaning.*

Suffering and health constitute the essential content, the substance, in the struggle of suffering and in the person's battle to survive, i.e., to continue to struggle, or to resign and not choose life.

There is a proverb that says that a person cannot appreciate health before she has encountered illness. There is some truth in this statement, which has its basis in the experience of people. It concerns awareness. We have found that suffering can give health a meaning through the fact that the person becomes aware of the contrasts and the different possibilities relevant to her own inner resources.

Regardless of the perspective there is a common denominator in all suffering: the person is in some sense cut off (reduced) from herself and her own wholeness. If we see health as wholeness (integration), suffering implies that this wholeness has been disturbed.

Conceptually and historically, health means wholeness and holiness.[1] Suffering and love are the deepest and most intimate movements of our soul and spirit and for that reason constitute the most fundamental of the life and health processes. Through suffering and love the person matures to a more multifaceted wholeness and to a deeper holiness, to life's wisdom and harmony or to be a more harmonious person. By holiness I am here alluding to a person's deep awareness of her uniqueness and responsibility as a fellow human being. By wholeness I mean a person's inseparable being as body, soul, and spirit.

In the deepest sense, health is wholeness through its association with suffering. If we consider suffering a natural part of the human being, suffering is also a part of health. We know that human suffering can become unendurable and our capacity for health can break down. Unendurable suffering paralyzes us and prevents our growth. *Health is compatible with endurable suffering.* A person who is involved in suffering that she experiences as endurable can simultaneously experience health. An open question remains whether this is true under all circumstances.

Health, in its deepest meaning, is an ontological concept, i.e., it deals with the individual person's *becoming* and *reality*.[2] The ontological health model is derived from health as *becoming* in relationship to a deeper wholeness, to an integration of a person's life. Health is seen as movement among three separate levels: health as *doing*, health as *being*, and health as *becoming*. Movement is expressed in the person's experience of various problems, needs or desires. At the *doing* level, health is evaluated by external objective criteria; on the level of *being*, people strive for a form of balance and harmony; and on the level of *becoming*, a person is not a stranger to suffering. She strives to reconcile herself with the circumstances of life and to be whole on a deeper level of integration. In our studies of suffering,[3] we found also that suffering can be understood on different levels, which coincide with the levels of health. (Figure 3)

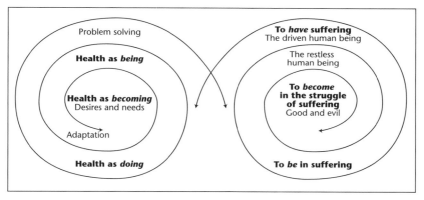

Figure 3. The Levels of Health and Suffering

There is a relationship among the various levels of health as well as in the strength and extent of the experience of suffering. Suffering can thus be experienced at three levels: to *have* suffering, to *be* in suffering, and to *become* in suffering.

1. To *have* suffering implies being a stranger to oneself and one's own inner desires, thereby even to one's own possibilities. It is to be driven and directed by external circumstances.

2. To *be* in suffering implies seeking something more harmonious. A person often experiences restlessness in the midst of an apparently restful environment. *Being* is experienced at least for a time as a state of happiness[4], harmony, and health. To *be*, however, is not enough. Stinissen (1990) presents the theory that through *being*, one can remain in the periphery of existence and there experience relative harmony, but the price one pays for this is denial of one's deepest self. The person may try to alleviate her suffering more shortsightedly through the satisfaction of needs. Needs may be satisfied, but the person will nonetheless experience an increased anxiety and she will sooner or later be driven further.

3. To *become* in suffering is a struggle, a struggle between good and evil, hope and hopelessness, between life and death. If life triumphs in this struggle, it leads to a higher level of integration, and the person can find meaning in her suffering.

Suffering can be unendurable independent of the level on which it appears. But the person often will not acknowledge her suffering as suffering if it emerges on the levels of "to *have*" or " to *be*." On the "to *have*" level the person flees from suffering and tries to explain it away. On the "to *be*" level the person seeks to triumph over it through satisfying her needs to a greater degree. Suffering and health constitute two different aspects of a person's life process. They are integrated with one another and are constantly present in the human experience. Depending on the circumstances, the person experiences varying degrees of suffering and/or health.

The Dynamic Whole

"…everything old has passed away; see,
everything has become new!" II Cor. 5:17

In order to understand the person's *becoming* in health and suffering it is necessary to introduce the distinctions between change and renewal. *Becoming* presupposes renewal. Change can occur on any and all levels.

Kierkegaard (1928, 30) speaks of the struggle of the elements when humility and pride are fused in a harmonic wholeness, "…and fortunate is the person for whom that is possible…" Kierkegaard means that the person in this wholeness has achieved "the archimedic point" from which she can lift the whole world; the point, just for that reason, must lie outside the world, outside the limitations of time and space. The person comes into a renewal and/or a transformation in the spiral of spiritual strength.[5]

Pauli (1930, 66, 67) maintains that this renewal is essential for the modern person.

> The modern person all too often lacks the *soul stuff* from which flows the ability to have pertinent interest in details, to experience compassion and shared joy, have peace and rest in one's existence, be able to wonder, become enchanted and offer oneself, to be able to believe and become joyful.

The person's archimedic point constitutes a source of strength that can be compared with her fundamental trust in someone or something else. This strength generates a longing for something that can be described as thirst (or hunger). The person seeks a source to quench this thirst. In the event the person finds a source that can quench the thirst, an increased longing to discover more of the secret of the source is born. The person's thirst increases and she tries once again to find her way to the source. This spiral continues, and deep within new strength is constantly generated. The spiral of spiritual strength advances through different movements. (Figure 4)

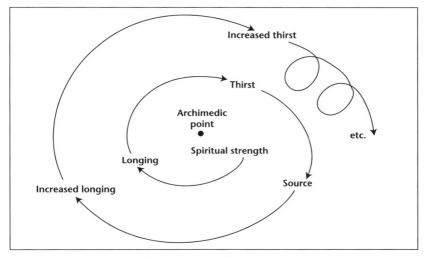

Figure 4. The Person's Spiral of Spiritual Strength

The basic life force, our vitality or the innermost movement (expression of life) gives an experience of desire or discomfort and the person feels a longing. By sensing this longing the person experiences thirst. The thirst initiates a seeking or striving for the source. Passion (the experience of desire at the source) gives birth to increased longing, and movement continues toward a higher awareness and *becoming* as a human being.

The basic life force, our vitality, is related to our ability to absorb nourishment and to be cleansed in body, soul, and spirit. This is related to our ability to perceive desire and uneasiness together with our reason, and to differentiate between good and evil. A person's ability to strive is given form in her desire, courage, and will and leads to actions and behavior, which constitute the motivational structure that underlies and directs the person's entire health behavior and actions. The motivational structure is determined by the underlying structures of meaning, the total life force, our vitality, and our attitude toward life.

One's development by no means always goes in a positive direction. A person is in constant movement and is being created or disintegrated (Bergson 1914) and is never ever completed. Development toward disintegration can imply that a person from the beginning perceives discomfort (suffers) and cannot identify the intrinsic thirst that is part of her being. The searching, which can be compared to the struggle of suffering, can lose its way and the person ends up at an impasse. If she arrives at the source, the experience of desire can be intensified and can be transformed to an evil passion which leads to increased suffering and death.

Suffering and Courage

Tournier (1983) states that courage is a stream in life which carries with it joy over battles that have been won. Courage is born in trials. A person needs courage to confront life and its trials. Courage can diminish suffering. Illness is always a life crisis. The person is aware that all things are transient. She feels placed before the face of God. The sick seek a cure and comfort but also understanding, love, and help at a deeper level.

Tournier maintains that one meaning in suffering exists in the human possibility to grow through suffering. Such growth, nevertheless, does not happen automatically. Through becoming courageous and using one's courage, a person can come to terms with her destiny. Joy breaks out when a person wins over her own destiny. The ability to accept one's own destiny is related to the person's maturity. It is a development toward a higher degree of freedom.

Courage and will are related. Ljunglund in his book, *The Affirmation of Life* (1914, 68) considers the question of the will. The external pressure to which a person is exposed can subdue her will.

> No one wants to deny the external pressure. It was there and is there naturally, but if one makes it into life's essence, it becomes intolerable, for then there is no help to be expected. If, on the other hand, we have freedom within us, we have the unquenchable and saving faith in its possible realization. And then it will be not pessimism but courage that life demands of us.

Time and again we return to a lack of freedom, the outward pressure of the driven person's suffering which has its foundation in the oppression and despair in the presence of this lack of freedom. The way out of this suffering demands courage and valor to follow one's own inner calling. This assumes, in turn, that the person dares to believe in her own possibilities, that life is sufficient, but that she also dares to believe that another person exists who can walk with her if the way becomes unendurable.

The Will or External Force In Health - The Meaning Of Health

Sometimes a person can experience suffering because she is forced to *have* or *be* in health. There are situations when the person must be able to remain in suffering, to be a patient and in a literal sense be passive or be set aside, which is an old-fashioned way of describing the patient. When a person is forced externally to manifest a health behavior, it erodes her strength from within. Health presupposes that the inner person wants health, i.e., finds meaning in *becoming*.

Becoming in health presupposes that the person has both the capacity and *substance* for health. The substance consists of virtue (Eriksson 1989). Health is a virtue and the capacity to transform substance so that it responds to the person's strivings. The person must at some level express her essence, her inner being.

Pauli (1930) presents the thought that a person's *becoming* is born in the struggle between evil and good. Her idea is that evil impulses that motivate evil actions are anchored in the more external layers of the soul. When religious and moral instincts awaken, self-awareness is moved inward to deeper layers and the good increasingly characterizes action. Here we can draw parallels to Aristotle's idea about our capacity to perceive the diverse expressions of body and soul (1987). Pauli's idea is that there is a *becoming* person within the individual.

> That which one finds and considers as one's self, one is forced unconsciously to express...hence we should not speak of a person as evil, not even about her good and evil self. But we could well speak of her becoming and her manifested self. (Pauli 1930, 29)

In suffering there is only one pervasive meaning and that is to survive. This survival can imply both increasing and decreasing growth. Every suffering implies in the deepest meaning a decreased growth in some respect. Outwardly the person may admit that the suffering has brought growth and has meaning. How often have we not sensed a deep agony among these people, the suffering that is hidden from every human soul.

The last escape route on which the innermost and most fragile part of us may be protected is to admit that suffering, in spite of everything, has meaning. The person does not have the strength to resist any longer. When a person is forced to admit that in spite of everything suffering has meaning, she has lost something of her innermost essence. She has come to this situation because she definitely is related to a concrete other and has no choice. This concrete relationship makes true suffering impossible because the sufferer must always yield to the "bystander" who cannot bear to see the other's suffering. We give our own suffering meaning so that the other shall be able to live. The "last compulsion" is to be forced to admit that our suffering has meaning. Each time we are confronted with that admission, we are suffocated a little bit, but we are simultaneously in a marvelous way lifted upwards through a narrow passageway and attain freedom, since we can only be forced in the upward direction. To suffer always implies relinquishing something. One relinquishes some of the potential with which one was born. Unfortunately, one has no choice. The choice is between survival (and to relinquish) and death (and eventually to receive).

NOTES

[1] See Eriksson (1976, 1989) about the concept of health. Our view of health and care has to an ever-greater extent become ahistorical. We have forgotten the historic reality and seek meaning here and now. An ahistorical view of health is reductionistic. Berdjajev (1990) believes that in the presence of a more ahistorical perspective culture surpasses civilization. Civilization is primarily technological and technology triumphs over the spirit. Specialization takes over and there is no cultural or spiritual wholeness. Quality is replaced by quantity. In civilization the consciousness of people is directed toward the means for life instead of toward life itself. Within culture a different will to remake life can emerge. Reflection is needed if a historical insight is to begin. In the historical perspective the person sees her own spiritual freedom and possibility to shape life.

[2] In the project *Multi-Dimensional Health* (Eriksson 1991; Eriksson and Herberts 1992) we have found that the so called "ontological health model," which has emerged recently, goes beyond the classical health models: the biological-static and the holistic. It has support both theoretically and empirically.

[3] Lindholm and Eriksson (1993 a,b) *Suffering and Love from a Psychiatric Perspective—A Case Study of the Encounter between Human Suffering and Love.*

[4] Nordenfelt (1991, 41-63) in his theory on health has brought out the concept of happiness, which he sees as a form of the second order's well-being. Happiness and joy come from reflection on life. Happiness is related to the fact that life has taken the form one desires it to have.

[5] The "Spiral of Spiritual Strength" has been presented as a "neutral" model. When it is to be applied, the model comes to be introduced in various contexts where different circumstances apply, often in the form of hindrances or frustrating factors. In this way the model is given various "colors," which express themselves in the terms used to describe the fundamental concepts. The model is given a more concrete content through seeking answers to the *what* and *how* questions. Through directing the *what* questions to vari-

ous individuals we get a description of different content in the model's components. The answer to the *how* question provides direction on methods, e.g., how do we perceive or show inability to perceive? How do we seek? The model that has eventually emerged, especially within the framework of our research in the theology of care, is hermeneutical. This implies that the open unanswered questions are formulated in hypotheses, which constitute the base for a new research process.

Chapter Ten

The Human Being's Attempt to Alleviate Suffering

…my God, my God, why have you forsaken me?

Matt. 27:46

In spite of the fact that suffering is a part of life, human beings do not want to suffer, but try in different ways to alleviate their suffering. One who bears an unendurable suffering often turns to God with the question, "Why?" There is even a contempt for suffering, and in modern civilization one does not want to give room for suffering. Richter (1979) believes that the total obliteration of suffering has been the primary goal in the striving for narcissistic omnipotence. In order to annihilate and escape suffering, the person develops different strategies.

In various studies and in the literature, the models by which the person attempts to alleviate suffering can be summarized as follows:

1. Annihilation of suffering; the person tries to eliminate the suffering.
2. Contempt for suffering; the person tries to raise herself above the suffering.
3. Flight from suffering; the person denies the existence of suffering and tries to flee or run away from it.
4. Resignation to suffering; the person has a fatalistic, deterministic, emotionally impoverished attitude in which suffering is accepted as an unavoidable evil.
5. Humility in the face of suffering; the person tries to find meaning in suffering.

Regardless of how the individual sees her suffering and what she feels may have caused it, the sufferer always strives to alleviate it in some way. The struggle of the person is to free herself from the unendurable suffering or to try to be reconciled to it. The person asks herself questions such as:

> How shall I live so as to find life's meaning?
> How shall I become free?

The struggle of the individual with her suffering is against evil, real or imagined. Our ability to encounter and alleviate human suffering is dependent on our own maturity in relation to our own suffering. To borrow Kierkegaard's words (1963), we shall encounter the individual's suffering as an individual. We shall look at the sufferings of the other without preconceived notions. We shall not compare it with something else, not try to explain or over-interpret it.

The Idea of Sacrifice

In the pre-Christian tradition people tried to buy themselves freedom from evil through making a sacrifice. Through sacrifice the person could appease the gods and prevent evil. The idea of sacrifice lives on in modern people despite its having assumed other forms.[1] We can all recognize ourselves in the fact that in the face of acute suffering we are prepared to sacrifice something in order to alleviate the suffering. Suffering can derive meaning through the possibility of sacrificing something.

Juchli (1991) describes the idea of sacrifice in an interesting way. She believes that through sacrifice we become closer to ourselves, others and God. The idea of sacrifice is closely related to the idea of reconciliation. The essential meaning of reconciliation, according to Nygren[2], is that conditions are created so that God and human beings can encounter one another. Nygren believes that in this perspective, history of religion is nothing more than an attempt to create these conditions through all sorts of cleansing, means of reconciliation, and sacrifices.

If we broaden the scope of reconciliation in the direction that Juchli presents, we can say that reconciliation implies a creation of conditions so that the person should be able to encounter herself, others and her God. We can also broaden this concept to include the person's existence as a whole. Against this background we can see humanity and the history of caring as various efforts to create the conditions for reconciliation and wholeness. In the perspective of suffering we see it as various efforts to overcome human suffering. Where suffering exists, there always also are love and possibilities. In judgment and sin, there is grace and reconciliation.

Nygren[3] differentiates among three stages in pre-Christian and non-Christian reconciliation and ways of thinking about sacrifice, and sees the Christian doctrine of reconciliation as a synthesis of these. We shall follow Nygren's reasoning and try to determine which parallels we can draw for today's person.

1. Sacrifice is a freely presented gift. Through sacrifice people seek to appease the angered deity and secure its blessing.
2. Obedience and the practice of righteousness is better than sacrifice. It is not anything external but the devotion of the heart that will accomplish reconciliation.
3. "…a broken and contrite heart, O God, you will not despise." (Psalm 51:17). When the person humbles herself and makes no pretense to have any worth, her misery is covered over and the way is opened to communion with God (compare with submission).

These assertions can be compared with different attempts to alleviate suffering. Is it perhaps so that the basis for our search for the meaning of suffering is in these assertions? Is it perhaps so that there is no confirmation and no suffering without sacrifice? And what is sacrifice? Is the person's sacrifice in order to get confirmation, the courage to dare to expose oneself, one's innermost being? Confirmation even presupposes a receiving and preparation for this.

In the case of severe suffering, or suffering which the person finds unendurable, we can see that the person tries to bring a sacrifice in order to atone for what she experiences as failure. In the same way we can see how the person becomes obedient and humbles herself and that in some way assumes a new inner attitude, which helps her to be reconciled with her life situation. The person ultimately humbles herself and is prepared to encounter the destiny that has befallen her. This can imply either reconciliation, which is a source for energy and development, or a situation where the person gives up and is no longer able to struggle against her destiny. Where is the line between giving up and struggling, and between seeing or not seeing the possibilities?

The Christian Doctrine of Reconciliation

The Christian doctrine of reconciliation may be seen as the completion of pre-Christian ideas and at the same time their radical revocation.[4] According to Nygren, it is not the person who brings her sacrifice to God and God who receives it, but it is God who offers Himself in Christ. "Christianity is the word of reconciliation, the message of how God has prepared a new way to us and for us into communion." No one expresses it more clearly than Paul in II Cor. 5:18.

Nygren believes that we can talk about two different forms of communion with God, depending on if we put the emphasis on God theocentrically, or on the person egocentrically. Egocentric reconciliation is characterized by the centrality of the ego and religion is understood from the perspective of desire. God is considered to be the highest good, the one who more than anyone can satisfy the desires and needs of people. In theocentric religion, God is everything. The person seeks God because God has made the person captive and she desires communion with God, not only to achieve grace.[5]

Nygren also addresses the question whether reconciliation occurs on the basis of holiness or sin. It is exactly at this point, according to Nygren, that the line is drawn between Christian and pre-Christian reconciliation doctrines.[6] Nygren believes that we are now at the point where the difference between Christian and non-Christian views of reconciliation emerges stronger than anywhere else. According to the Lutheran view, God seeks fellowship with sinners. The person does not need to justify herself before God in order to enter communion with God. *Sola fides* implies communion with God on the basis of sin. It is through this that theocentric reconciliation's faith is completed.

Sacrifice, Reconciliation and Love

Reconciliation comes from God's love. Reconciliation and love are essentially one and the same. God's love seeks and desires communion with the sinner and the lost. Nygren asks himself the question if God's love does not make reconciliation unnecessary. The person cannot by herself achieve reconciliation through any sort of sacrifice. Reconciliation is entirely God's act. At this point one can ask oneself if not all reconciliation has been abolished. Nygren here directs the argument to the conclusion that it is precisely the love of God that makes reconciliation necessary.[7]

Nygren also believes that the deepest secret of reconciliation exists between God's love and the selfish world. Something must be sacrificed in order for these to be made one. It is not selfishness that is sacrificed, but it is divine love that takes the sacrifice upon itself.[8]

Hope In Suffering
Hope is kindled like a flickering longing in a wounded soul.

Suffering gives birth to a feeling of hopelessness, and suffering needs hope to be alleviated. Our hope is linked to a form of mutual giving and taking, of helping and being helped. Hope in suffering exists in the knowledge that we can conquer suffering only by going through suffering.[9] Perhaps that gives us courage to dare to enter suffering.

A person's basic attitude toward her own suffering oscillates between humility and bitterness. Humility is a virtue that helps the person to dare go through her suffering. When one encounters her own suffering the capacity to be compassionate is born, helping the person to see the other and to turn away from the self. In contrast, bitterness leads to hatred and contempt toward oneself and others. Bitterness makes compassion impossible and spreads an atmosphere of evil.

Pauli (1938) emphasizes the significance of the attitude a person assumes toward her suffering. It can be active or passive. The passive attitude easily leads to resignation, and the suffering is extended. When the person's soul is actively focused, suffering is not allowed to become a subject and the person herself does not become an object for suffering.

It is just at this point that the struggle against suffering receives its meaning. When suffering becomes a subject, the person is subordinated to her suffering and suffering becomes an accepted part of life. An active struggle does not allow the person to be consumed by the suffering and become an object of that suffering. When suffering becomes a subject, it occupies one's life. Life should not be subordinated to suffering. Rather, the living, struggling person makes suffering to be an object for her life struggle. Suffering cannot be a goal for a person's life.

Since suffering can be made into a means for something deeper and more comprehensive, the person's *becoming*, it can also generate activity, a striving for more life. Pauli (1938) speaks of a life-hunger that has its foundation in a life-trust, a deep trust that is deeper than the will to live. It is not enough to will, since the will is often associated with fear and anxiety, but the person must believe. Life can only be furthered if there is faith, a trust in life itself.

Suffering can be alleviated regardless of whether the person's basic orientation is characterized by humility or bitterness. We have many descriptions of how patients, next of kin and caregivers try to alleviate even the most severe suffering. The foundation lies in love. Regardless of the way in which suffering expresses itself, love is the fundamental power that is needed to alleviate suffering. The foundations of caring – faith, hope, and love[10] – have been shown to be the foundation in the struggle to alleviate suffering.

To Be Comforted

"That which exists and is good has the capacity to provide comfort." Meister Eckhart

To try to alleviate suffering and provide comfort is something we always can do. Nevertheless, it seems that we have lost some of this capacity. Comfort relieves a person's pain and anguish in suffering that is experienced as unendurable. True comfort awakens in the suffering person confidence and trust in the good, and gives courage and hope. In comfort there must be room for both weariness of life and hope.

What Can The Person Herself Do?

If the person has courage and strength, she can try to struggle. However cruel the suffering is, the person should have the possibility to maintain her dignity. To be able to smile when the heart weeps, but at the same time know that there is a loving embrace in which to seek refuge — this is something which confirms the person and gives her the courage to struggle on. There are moments when a person lacks the strength to smile and tears take over. To weep does not mean that we have lost our dignity. To encounter a person's weeping is to meet something of the holy (deeply whole and honorable), and we should receive this with reverence and respect, without constraint and question. To be able to weep in dignity implies that we are not burdened with "why?" and the demand for explanations. It demands humility and unconditional love from another human being in order to make room for this. I think it is often difficult for us to give this kind of room because we ourselves have not experienced it and feel a deep longing for it. It is difficult to see another person receive something that one longs for deeply, and it is even more difficult to be able to share joy with that person. Our own suffering becomes too difficult in this moment, and if there is no one in this situation who understands this suffering, the feeling of inadaquacy may generate actual hatred.

The suffering human being, in the deepest sense, is at the mercy of other people, for it is on them she is dependent in her daily life. What an individual can accomplish for herself is dependent on others. There comes a moment when a person actually discovers her absolute solitude through the insight that it is only she who can do something. The moment she discovers this, she may stand before the greatest suffering. It is then that the choice must be made to struggle, or to resign and enter an empty solitude. The person can choose to make her suffering a means for growth and development, or into a limiting factor. The prerequisite for suffering as being a means of growth is that the person receives confirmation of her suffering. Suffering is confirmed by the person sharing it with another, abstract or concrete.

To truly be able to transform suffering to positive energy presupposes that we can share it through story with another person. To truly be able to share the deepest secrets, that which weighs us down most of all and perhaps frightens us and causes us to condemn ourselves, gives power to the transformation.[11] What it involves here, as in the confessional, is finding a person worthy of our confidence and trust.

It surprised us in our research that when we asked what patients and "ordinary" people did to alleviate their suffering, they had difficulty answering this question.[12] They thought that the person herself is unable to do anything to alleviate the suffering. How does this attitude develop? Does it have its foundation in disappointment and lack of trust, or is it a sign of resignation, or is it that without God a person can do nothing?

There certainly are moments when a person would gladly share her secrets and burdens with someone else, but she sees that nothing exists except a large heavy empty space within her. The experience of this total emptiness gives the feeling of being dead though alive. What can a person do to fill this empty space? At this moment, total resignation is near. I mean that a form of holy experience is needed to fill the emptiness and give life meaning. This holy experience can take place through an encounter with nature, art, a person or God. The essential thing is that the experience has the capacity to reach the person's innermost longing and to create a new hunger for life, that in spite of everything, life has meaning.

NOTES

[1] Among others Kübler-Ross (1972) states that in the face of serious illness and the threat of death the person is prepared to sacrifice to get life and freedom from suffering. She realizes that human suffering from a historic and Christian point of view has an important significance for the person. Today's society, however, denies the meaning of suffering and avoids encountering the phenomenon. Kübler-Ross looks critically at technological development and the prevailing value systems in the western world that, according to her, have increased suffering to a large degree and at a cost to humanity. According to her, this development implies that we simultaneously have become less humane, and in spite of increased numbers of well trained personnel in the health care field, patients' suffering and loneliness are increased. She asks, "What is happening in a community where a high IQ is preferred to humane treatment of suffering?"

[2] See Nygren (1932, 10). Nygren is critical of religion and maintains that there is limited understanding of what is really involved when one considers various doctrines of reconciliation as more external decoration rather than what really makes possible a communion between God and human beings.

[3] (ibid. 8-9) Nygren believes that the characteristic for the intellectualist-metaphysical concept of religion is to let religion be absorbed in a religious worldview. If it is only a question of a religious worldview or metaphysical ideas about God and his essence, we can occupy ourselves with such concerns without the question of reconciliation ever becoming an actuality.

The meaning of religion is communion with God. If we have come to clarity in this question, the reconciliation will become the most important of all. Religion wants to mediate a real meeting between God and persons. Therefore reconciliation becomes an inescapable question for religion. Nygren believes that in reality this is the innermost question. Wherever the person feels herself standing before God, her God awareness becomes an awareness of judgment. To stand before God is to feel oneself both clean and as a sinner.

⁴"The cross of Christ stands as a seal of the truth that it does not depend only on human imagination when the need for reconciliation constantly rises anew within humanity. There is a need for real reconciliation between God and humankind." The Christian reconciliation doctrine parallels the pre-Christian idea, "No communion with God without reconciliation, no reconciliation without sacrifice."

Nygren (1932, 14-15) maintains that we cannot understand the Christian reconciliation theory as a fourth stage completing the three pre-Christian ones. On that way of thinking we have gone from the center of religious life. There is nothing else to be sacrificed and yet in spite of this, Nygren claims we have not reached actual reconciliation. In every type of sacrifice there is something that makes it insufficient as a means of reconciliation. "Humility as a unified achievement is the greatest possible self-contradiction" (p. 15). That would imply that the person tries to assert herself before God.

⁵ Nygren believes that we can differentiate between an egocentric non-Christian and a theocentric Christian doctrine of reconciliation. The first emanates from the person and leads back to her. The second emanates from God and leads back to God who has reconciled us with himself through Christ.

⁶ (ibid. 16-28) "…Reconciliation does not mean that we, by ourselves or through some substitute, climb up out of our human, sinful life to the divine sphere and enter into communion with God and meet him, so to say, on his own level. Rather, reconciliation means that God descends to our level and communicates with us there, in spite of our sin."

⁷ (ibid. 52-57) Nygren draws the conclusion that reconciliation is a synthesis between God's holiness and God's love and formulates it in the following manner: "Not because God's love is holy, but because it is love, reconciliation is necessary."

⁸ (ibid. 49-50) "It was God who in Christ reconciled the world to Himself." Nygren believes that here, in a literal sense, we can talk about a substitutionary sacrifice or suffering.

⁹ Jung (1981) says that the Western person has tried to solve the problem of suffering by suppressing it with medication, while the Eastern person tries to be freed from suffering by giving up.

¹⁰ (Eriksson 1990, Lindholm and Eriksson 1993 a, b) *The Home* is a living illustration of these strivings. See also Chapter 11 in this book.

¹¹ Jung (1981) believes that it is important for the human soul to share its deepest secrets with someone else. The secrets we share with no one are harmful for the soul if one is aware of these secrets.

¹² Eriksson (1993). *Encounters with Suffering.*

Chapter Eleven

Suffering in Caring and Health Care

"Yes. There is beauty
There is love.
There is joy.
All you who suffer from the world's
misery defend them."

Eeva Kilpi

From a historical perspective caring and different kinds of caring organizations have developed for the purpose of alleviating human suffering. Paradoxically, in many instances today, this development instead has resulted in suffering for the human being, the patient. We undeniably confront a situation in which we must take a new position relative to the fundamental premises for caring.

In this section of the book I want to present the suffering which exists and which we encounter today in caring.[1] To find ways of eliminating or at least tangibly alleviating suffering may be seen as the greatest challenge for caring research and caring science in the immediate future. In the concluding chapter I shall discuss the new paradigm within caring, a humanistic paradigm where the core of theory is shifted from illness to suffering.

We encounter three different forms of suffering in caring:

1. *The suffering of illness: suffering experienced in relation to illness and treatment.*
2. *The suffering of care: suffering experienced in the actual caring situation.*
3. *The suffering of life: suffering experienced in relation to one's own unique life*—to live or not to live; insights about absolute aloneness and loneliness.

We shall examine more closely the different forms of suffering in caring and health care. Often they overlap with one another and it may be difficult to differentiate between them in an actual situation. Through describing them one by one we can get a deeper understanding of the different forms of suffering and increased possibilities to recognize them, and eventually be able to alleviate suffering in actual caring situations.

The Suffering Of Illness

We have always known that illness and treatment can cause suffering, primarily through the pain inflicted upon the patient. Pain, often bodily pain, is a common cause of suffering related to illness. Illness is not necessarily accompanied by pain and, as indicated earlier, pain is not identical with suffering. Nevertheless, the relationship between pain and suffering is central, and unendurable suffering can be alleviated by our effort to reduce pain. Bodily pain is often focused in a definite part of the body and captures the person's total attention, which makes it more difficult for her to use her entire potential to master suffering. Bodily pain can be unendurable and drive the person to a mental and spiritual death. Bodily pain should be alleviated with all available means.

Less discussed in the literature is the mental and spiritual suffering that illness and treatment can cause. Stratton[2] uses the concept "clinical suffering," a suffering apparent to caregivers and a direct consequence of illness. Clinical suffering can best be compared with our concept of the suffering of illness. The latter can be divided into the following categories:

1 *Bodily pain* caused by illness and treatment. The pain is seldom only bodily pain, but is experienced by the whole person. By bodily pain we should understand that it is pain, and thereby suffering, which besets the person and can be perceived as physical suffering. When a person experiences intense physical suffering, a great deal of her attention is concentrated on this.

2. *Mental and spiritual suffering*. This suffering is caused by the experience of humiliation, shame, and/or guilt that a person experiences in relation to her illness or treatment. This can partly be experienced by the patient herself, partly arise because of a condemnatory attitude from the caregiver, or be caused by the social context. This form of suffering is similar to what we have called the suffering of care.

Lazare (1992) maintains that minimal interest has been manifested in discussing questions that relate to the person's experience of shame and humiliation in connection with illness and treatment. Lazare distinguishes between shame and humiliation and argues that shame is more of a feeling within the person, whereas humiliation is most often associated with an experience in relation to others. In both, the person is characterized as something smaller and less than she thought and hoped for. She does not attain her own personal ideals. Guilt emerges from a feeling that she has transgressed certain limits and she experiences ill-being. This feeling develops when a person feels that perhaps she has caused illness and suffering by not living in the right way.

Lazare believes that people often are subjected to shame, guilt, and humiliation in health care. Illness and treatment can be responsible for this. The experience of shame varies within different medical specialties. In the care of children, it is often the parents who experience shame and guilt because they have caused their children's illness and suffering and have been unable to provide good care for their children. When it involves skin ailments, a person's suffering can be publicly visible, and in gynecology a person's most intimate areas are invaded. If a person has stomach ailments her illness is often related to psychosomatic problems and she feels guilt and shame from showing psychological weakness.

Many expressions, concepts, and names for illnesses are even derogatory, e.g., that one is "infertile," "sterile," "narcissistic," "borderline," "malignant" and "disabled" or "handicapped." There is also stigmatization, a labeling of people, for example, on the basis of status as well as deviant behavior of some type.

An absurd description from our research is a young schoolgirl's story of how she was shamed by her first menstruation. She had not been able to talk about it with her parents or siblings. She lay in bed unhappy with stomach cramps and tried secretly to manage her change of sanitary napkins. She felt unclean and filled with shame.

There are many situations within health care where the person is exposed to shame and humiliation. These can involve different events in illness and treatment or the patient's own experience of feeling a failure as a patient, not being able to cooperate in her treatment. The whole system of caring for the sick can be the cause of feelings of shame and humiliation. One is forced to find her way to information, stand in line, wait, ask, and use common public space for the most personal functions.

Suffering among the elderly is especially obvious within institutional care. In a study in the United States by Starck and McGovern (1992)[3] it has been demonstrated that all elderly who are in an institution suffer in some respect. The worst time is when the older person seeks to adjust to the institution. Suffering is interpreted as losses of various kinds. One loses one's personal abilities, close friends and associates, participation in social groups, one's home and one's full value as a human being.

Many situations in health care cause suffering for close relatives. Sometimes their suffering can be more difficult than that of the patients. This suffering has not received enough attention. In a real sense relatives are also patients and in need of care and help.

A relative who suffers cannot suffer with the patient. This inability can cause feelings of shame and guilt and/or aggression and despair. The following descriptions give a picture of how the hospital and the entire patient situation can be experienced.[4]

> Papa often says that time is so long, these white walls are
> so dreary to look at unendingly. Sometimes it seems strange
> to sit and hear all the sounds outside the door, these people

who move back and forth. Will someone come in? But no, most often they pass by. I used to think that those who lie here perhaps get used to it. Perhaps they don't hear the approaching steps in the same way after several years.

I remember when father was diapered just a day or so after he came here. At home he could handle going to the bathroom even though he fell often. It was for that reason he came here. He was very much embarrassed and denied that he was using a diaper when I asked, even though I saw it. After just a week he announced happily, "See, I have a diaper and don't have to go to the bathroom because then I fall." I felt sorry for him. I am not sure he was so glad. Perhaps he pretended. On the other hand, he has always been able to adjust. (A relative)

The Suffering Of Care

The suffering associated with care is not a common phenomenon in the literature. Is it actually so that suffering of care is a phenomenon typical of caring and health care in the 1990s? Much points in this direction, especially the increasing research and discussion regarding ethical questions of caring, the definition of what is good care, as well as quality assurance within caring and health care.

It is interesting, but not surprising, to know that Florence Nightingale actually describes the suffering associated with care and protests against it.

…the nerves of the sick suffer from seeing the same walls, the same ceiling, the same surroundings during a long confinement to one or two rooms. (Nightingale, 1859, 33; 1954, 72)

How little the real sufferings of illness are known or understood. How little does any one in good health fancy him or even herself into the life of a sick person. (1859, 57; 1954, 166)

Nightingale states further how loneliness, anxiety, uncertainty and waiting, as well as fear of surprises, cause suffering. Above all, Nightingale opposes the attitude about suffering and illness that prevails among nurses. The nurse asks herself if any care can protect the patient from unnecessary suffering and if any illness can be free of pain. Nightingale believes that there is no answer for this question but maintains that suffering is not a symptom of illness but evidence of insufficient care.

There are many forms of suffering associated with caring and health care, and every person who has been exposed to suffering caused by caring, or by lack of caring, experiences it in her own way. The suffering of care can be summarized in the following major categories:

1. Violation of the patient's dignity
2. Condemnation and punishment
3. Assertion of power
4. Omitted care or non-caring

Violation of the Patient's Dignity

Violation of a patient's dignity and worth as a human being constitutes the most frequently occurring form of suffering of care, and all other forms can be derived from this one. To violate a patient's dignity implies taking from her the possibility to be a whole and complete person. This also reduces the possibility for her to use her innermost health resources. Violation of a person's dignity can occur through direct and concrete actions, e.g., nonchalance in conversation or carelessness in protecting the patient during care activities that involve intimate areas or personal questions. Violation can also occur more abstractly through a deficient ethical demeanor, or failure to "see" the person or give her a place.

The Concept of Dignity

The concept of dignity has several dimensions. Dignity involves having worth, but dignity and worth are not synonymous concepts. Conceptually the term dignity has an inner and an outer dimension.[5] With the inner dimension we associate trustworthiness, sense of honor, and morality. With the outer we associate characteristics such as glory, rank, status, office, nobility, appearance, and reputation. All human beings in the deepest sense have the same dignity and worth but also have their own understanding of their dignity. Both inner and outer dignity are parts of the individual as a human being.

The following main categories that have relevance for caring can also be derived:

1. Dignity is associated with high human office. This is related to equality and trustworthiness. It is one's absolute worth as a human being.
2. Dignity is a state with a more relative or subjective meaning. This may include both the worth a person confers on herself, self-respect, and the worth conferred by others or derived from a system of norms.

Dignity as high office. The person's absolute dignity is given her in that she has received a high office, or *call to serve.* In biblical terms the person has received her dignity because she was created in God's image. The person experiences absolute dignity when she can fulfill her responsibility as a human being, i.e., she can serve and exist for another. When a person is deprived of responsibility, she is simultaneously robbed of her dignity. To human dignity belongs the freedom to choose and the right to protect oneself from intrusion.

Trustworthiness implies that as a person and as a patient one is taken seriously and one's experiences are considered true. In trustworthiness there is also an aesthetic dimension that expresses itself in proper, correct, and respectable action.

Dignity as worth. For various reasons, human beings are ascribed differing worth and they experience their worth differently. We have maintained earlier that the patient may experience herself as worthless because of shame or guilt, and that caregivers look differently at patients and ascribe different worth to them. To experience that one has personal worth even as a patient is of fundamental significance for one's health. All forms of violation of the patient's dignity imply a type of suffering. It is the caregiver's responsibility to give the patient the possibility to experience her full worth and to prevent all forms of violation.

Von Post[6] has determined in a study of perioperative care that the dignity of both patient and caregiver is violated. Violation of the patient's dignity takes place when natural caring is omitted, and the caregivers who experience this simultaneously feel violated. She also points out the significance of the patient's dignity being confirmed in the process of caring.

Åhgren[7] in his book *Paralysis* gives a good description of when one does not feel totally worthy:

> ...to one whose life is vegetating, a wish to once again be a fully worthy member of society as the only meaningful thing in life is meaningless and destructive. Death becomes finally the only logical alternative, but is impossible to attain when one cannot even raise one's eyebrows.

Notations in Åhgren's diary constitute a frightening description of the struggle of a suffering human being who is not seen and confirmed by caregivers. Everything becomes meaningless, even the entries in the diary. Not to be seen, or to be considered to be someone one is not, nor wants to be, is a violation and breeds feelings of shame, guilt, and despair.

From Åhgren's diary we can see how he experienced the condemnation of the doctors. His greatest suffering was his inability to speak or to communicate with people around him. During the first days of his illness, the chief physician at each round would state, "And here we have the man who refuses to speak." (1986, 27)

It is clear from Åhgren's description that all the usual daily occurrences have an unbelievably great significance. He describes how he longs for fresh water, and a glass is placed on his table, but he can't reach it:

> One day a nurse came in and complained that I drank too little. My kidneys would suffer, she said. How do you respond to this when you can't speak? (1986, 9)

Åhgren gives a graphic description of how it feels when one day you suddenly lack the ability to change your own bodily position and you become totally dependent on others for every little detail. One understands then that even bed-making and morning hygiene can be a type of suffering.

To confirm the dignity of human beings in caring implies that every patient be given individualized care. It does not imply that one gives inequitable care. The concept that everyone needs the same care is misleading. To confirm the dignity of human beings presupposes that one dares to be different in relation to patients' differences, and yet in all situations confirm each and everyone's innermost dignity.

A patient's relative describes how it feels when one's dignity is violated:

> The caregivers contacted me and wanted me to come and discuss my mother's continued care with them and the doctors in the department. We discussed forced feeding and intravenous infusion treatment. It was difficult to share in the discussions and to take a position, but it was also gratifying to be present and help make the decision. We came to the decision that we should continue with the feeding as long as possible and not be too concerned about the quantity of food for each day.
>
> I saw that mother suffered. Around her mouth and eyes she developed a strained look and she tensed the muscles in her jaws. Tears glistened in the corners of her eyes and now and then dropped down her cheeks. I think that she felt powerless when she noticed that we did not take into con-

sideration that she tried to resist. First we tried feeding with a teaspoon, then we opened her jaws with one finger and inserted the spoon; then we tried with a large syringe to squirt in liquid nourishment into her mouth. This felt awful and I asked them to try it on me so that I might feel how it felt or have a little understanding about how it felt.

What I thought of at first was that this feels so humiliating, so powerless, so violating and impersonal in some sense. It seemed as if no one cared, that one had no value. My will meant nothing, but at the same time I knew that it was for my sake, for my good, but it is hard to describe the conflicting feelings I had.

Condemnation and Punishment

Condemnation and punishment are closely linked with the violation of human dignity, but here I would like to emphasize them as a special category since one so often encounters condemnation in caring. This condemnation has its origin in the understanding that it is the caregiver's task to decide what is right or wrong with respect to the patient. With the authority of factual knowledge, the caregiver can naturally judge what would be best for the patient under certain conditions, but the patient always has the freedom to choose for herself. There is also an understanding about how the "ideal" patient should be, and the one who does not comply can feel some condemnation.

Condemnation and punishment often belong together. One way to punish is to omit caritative care or be indifferent toward the patient. Punishment through indifference can express itself in the caregiver neglecting to wipe the mouth of the patient after feeding when the patient lacks the strength to do it. At the same time this is a deep humiliation for the patient. Many times I have experienced the feeling of humiliation and punishment that an older patient experiences when the caregivers no longer have the energy to converse with a patient they perceive as difficult or troublesome. In the same way that a quick caress of an elderly face can give the day a gold lining, an omitted look can extinguish the last spark of the desire for life and joy.

Assertion of Power

To assert power is a way of causing suffering for the other. To assert power is to deprive the other of her freedom, since one forces her to do things she would not choose to do of her own free will. We know that there exists a negative assertion of power within the caring community, but presently we have relatively little systematic knowledge of this.

The assertion of power can be either direct or indirect. Not to take the other, i.e., the patient, seriously is to assert power. When a person is not taken seriously, she is not valued, and this gives her a feeling of powerlessness. There are many descriptions of this kind of assertion of power.

To assert power in the act of caring may mean that one forces patients to do things that they actually are unable to do. One deprives the patient of the right to be a patient. Fant describes in the book *The Last Years* (1991, 133) a situation in which the caregiver asserts power against her mother:

> Mother had fallen out of bed and broken two ribs because she did not dare to call for help to get up. Now she was on her way to the toilet and two caregivers were present and watched but did not support her. When the doctor asked why the mother had been exposed to this humiliation, he got the reply that exercise in walking was beneficial.

The use of power emerges in many different situations and in various degrees. Quite often it is expressed when caregivers want to hold to established routines and find it difficult to share the patient's thinking. The direct exercise of power is evident in different kinds of coercive acts of caring. More indirect power is reflected in attitudes of the caregiver, which force the patient to act contrary to her will.

Omitted Caring or Non-Caring

Omitted caring can be due to a lack of ability to see and determine what the patient needs. Non-caring, that is to say, a situation where one perhaps does not perform caring or where the caring dimension is absent, often has its origin in basic attitudes and in the experience of the motive for caring.

There are many forms of omitted caring, from minor kinds of oversight and carelessness to conscious direct acts of neglect. Omitted caring, non-caring, or lack of good caring have been investigated in several studies. Halldorsdottir[8] describes five basic modes of being with the patient that extend from caring to uncaring. She presents a continuum from life-giving to life-destroying care. Life-destroying and the life-limiting care contain many of the factors we have found related to the various forms of suffering in caring.

The following description is an example of omitted caring or non-caring experienced by a nursing student.[9]

> The suffering man was old. He had been unable to urinate after surgery, which caused him suffering. He also had suffering associated with his illness and had postoperative pain as well as back pain because he had to lie flat in bed.
>
> One time he rang the bell and asked to be catheterized. It was five minutes before reporting time and no caregiver went to him. He had to lie for forty-five minutes feeling the need to urinate and ready to explode.
>
> After this, the patient began to "whine" about the poor care, and the caregivers responded every time he rang for them by waiting especially long before they came. It seemed as if the caregivers were punishing him because he couldn't urinate and because he berated them. They punished him with omitted care, forcing him to wait a long time before he was given care.

Omitted caring implies a violation of a person's dignity and is even a way to exert power over the powerless.

Suffering of Life

Illness, poor health, and the situation of being a patient affect the total life of a person. The life one is accustomed to is disturbed and suddenly more or less taken away. The person confronts suffering that encompasses her total life situation. The suffering of life can include everything from a threat to one's total existence to a loss of the possibility to pursue varied social tasks. The suffering of life is a suffering related to everything included in what it means to live, to be a human being among other human beings.

To Be Annihilated

To be threatened by annihilation, to feel that one will die but not know when, is an enormous suffering. Not to be seen is also a way of being annihilated. Silbersky describes this in his book, *And Time Stood Still* (1992):

> I am afraid, more afraid than ever…afraid of death…of the end…of the pain. I want to live…I must be permitted to live…I have an obligation to live.

The threat of annihilation, fear and despair are mingled with the will to live, a fighting spirit. A person's total life situation can be changed in many ways. Physical suffering and severe pain cause a paralysis of the whole person. A sudden forced change in a person's life situation is contrary to nature and the person needs time to find a new context of meaning.

A person who has experienced herself as whole may suddenly feel that her identity has been disintegrated and she feels like a collection of parts with a disintegrated inner core. Dahl (1975) describes this in her book, *When I Was Sick*, "Suffering can be being tired and weary of one's sick and evil body, of one's entire self."

Perhaps one of the deepest forms of the suffering of life is lack of love. We constantly are given new examples of how lack of love kills and annihilates a person. Ahlin (1907) has captured this cruelty in his book *Your Life's Fruit*. Johannes is the main character in the book and his suffering is that he constantly seeks his mother's love but without a response. When he is in his late teen years his mother dies, and then for the first time he feels relief since now he can cease hoping for a response to his love. In the midst of his sorrow he feels a liberation.

To Give Up

To lack strength and to give up in the face of a seemingly hopeless situation is something we often encounter in caring.[10] The feeling of giving up can be caused by the patient's lack of strength to continue the struggle. The patient can experience a lack of worth or mission in life. When we confront a patient with severe suffering, an incurable illness and perhaps the weight of weariness of life, it feels tremendously difficult to know what we should do. It is in situations like this that questions about euthanasia are often raised.[11] A student reports:

> Two summers ago I cared for an old woman who had lost hope and the desire to live. We tried as caregivers to encourage and support her in every way and always to be present when she needed help.

> During the summer she had lost her appetite. We tried to provide her with her favorite dishes in small portions and with good desserts. We tried to feed her with a large spoon, teaspoon, and syringe, which I personally felt was a humiliating way to feed her. One could see in her eyes and facial expression that she was suffering. Her relatives also suffered but at the same time wanted her to be fed forcibly. It hurt me to see a person suffer so unbearably and to see that she had lost hope and the desire to live. Toward the end of the

summer she died and that was her wish. We had tried with forced feeding and with intravenous procedures to keep her alive. But the lady died and I believe that she had lost her hope and the desire to live because of her unendurable suffering.

Suffering Can Be Alleviated

We should strive to eliminate unnecessary suffering, but there is a suffering that cannot be eliminated and which we must do all we can to alleviate. The prerequisite for being able to alleviate suffering is to create a culture of caring in which the patient feels welcomed, respected, and cared for. This is a culture of caring in which the patient experiences the right and the space to be a patient. Our studies have demonstrated that suffering can be alleviated and that often it is a question of simple, daily activities within caring.

To alleviate a patient's suffering involves first of all not violating her dignity, not condemning, or abusing power, but instead giving the care the patient needs. It is so easy to overlook apparently small details, but they are so important for the patient who is dependent on a caregiver. The need to show respect and to confirm a patient's dignity is apparent in situations where the patient must carry out her most intimate needs in the presence and with the help of others. Offering patients the possibility of washing hands, brushing teeth, using deodorant, or combing their hair can give them new strength and a feeling of worth as human beings.

Even the most difficult suffering can be alleviated for a time by a friendly look, a word, a caress or something else that expresses an honest feeling of compassion. A person who suffers needs acts of love over and over again. In all suffering there is also a glimmer of delight that can increase through our ability to "play" and laugh together. Play in suffering, if artistically applied, can be an expression of love and can alleviate suffering.

Our studies show that there are many ways to alleviate suffering. Caregivers try to alleviate it by doing something concrete for the patient, partly by being available and entering into a relationship. Here are some examples of how caregivers have alleviated patients' suffering:

- The basic attitude should be that we desire to alleviate suffering.
- Cleanliness of the body is alpha and omega – first and last. A person who feels unclean suffers, feels unworthy as a person, and

does not want to be in contact with others.

- To be present, to express "I am here if you need me." This means not having to question or ask for an explanation.
- To converse and share.
- To encourage, support, comfort.
- To communicate hope but also share hopelessness.
- To be honest.
- To fulfill the patient's wishes.
- To support the patient in his or her faith – the power of faith.

Patients do not always experience that their suffering could have been alleviated, but they have thoughts about how it should be done. The thoughts and wishes of patients are consistent with those mentioned previously, i.e., to protect human worth and to experience and feel that one is respected and cared for. Patients do not experience fear of being without relief in relation to illness and treatment, e.g., in terms of pain relief; they are more fearful of being despised, alone, abandoned, and without another's response. They think they can find relief by being out in nature and near plants and animals, but they express a clear need of another's love and trust.

It is most important for the caregiver to dare to encounter suffering, to go straight toward it or right through it with the patient. One caregiver in our research expresses it as follows:

> I think the answer to the question if suffering can be allevi-
> ated depends on if I can meet the patient and in the meet-
> ing, dare make myself available... I do not avoid eye contact
> with the patient, and when the patient says that he feels
> dirty, I don't say, "Then go and wash yourself." Rather, I re-
> ally listen and I dare to consider how it feels to be dirty, and
> dare to identify with the patient, dare to share the patient's
> feelings...or dare go in and acknowledge the patient so that
> he may weep. I dare stand by your side even though you
> are weeping, or stand here even if you fall. I shall see that
> you are fed. I shall lead you to the table and I shall feed you.
> Then I believe that there is a genuineness in this also...not
> to withdraw myself from the patient even though I am prob-
> ably trembling within, or inwardly feeling aggressive.

Åhgren (1992, 12) maintains that the only way to deal with one's suf-
fering is to try to endure it. When one reads patients' descriptions of how they try to alleviate their suffering, one is astonished by the struggle and the inventiveness generated by suffering. At the same time one feels humility before the person. One also experiences anger in the face of the

powerlessness and the limitations found in the caring process, but also gratitude for all caregivers who struggle against suffering.

Our experience of how suffering can be alleviated may be summarized under the following points:

1. Through the development of the culture of caring and the hospital milieu. Suffering can be alleviated when the patient feels welcome, invited, and that he or she has a place. Through being informed, participating, and getting answers to their questions, patients' anxiety and uneasiness can be reduced.

2. Through the patient's feeling loved, confirmed, and understood. He or she is met with dignity and experiences the right to be a patient and to have time and space to suffer. At the same time the patient has a shared responsibility as a person.

3. Through getting the care and treatment that the illness and the person as a unique individual needs.

Why Is There Suffering In Caring?
*The goal of caring cannot be health but must reach
further, encompassing human life as a whole.
To exist for someone else, to serve, is to live the meaning in
one's life. To restore the human being to service is the
ultimate goal of caring.*

Suffering in caring may be seen as unnecessary suffering that by all means should be eliminated. When one reads the various descriptions of suffering in caring, one is easily filled with a feeling of hopelessness and feels shame about being a professional caregiver. However, we do not know the innermost causes of suffering in caring. We must continue to study this to understand it and to penetrate into it. To a degree I believe that we—all categories of professional caregivers—many times unconsciously cause suffering in caring. That is the result of an absence of reflection and a lack of knowledge of human suffering. Our view of reality in caring is still shaped by a reductionistic and illness-centered perspective. We are still dominated by advanced technology and thus forget the human being (see Kemp 1991). Suffering in caring has to do with the ethics of caring and with good caring. I believe that when we consciously strive for good care, a care that in the deepest sense is ethical, i.e., has its foundation in love and responsibility for the other, we can largely eliminate the unnecessary suffering in caring. Perhaps suffering in caring exists so that we become even more aware of all the good that, in spite of everything, exists?

NOTES

[1] In the book *The Hidden Dimension of Illness; Human Suffering* edited by Starck and McGovern, suffering related to both illness and treatment describes suffering in caring even if they do not use the term "suffering in caring." Johannisson (1992,117) in Kallenberg (ed.) *The Meaning of Suffering* considers another form of suffering, the naked suffering, which she sees as the purely bodily suffering that has been stripped of every metaphysical dimension. It is the suffering that encompasses all different forms of suffering in caring. In naked suffering the person is totally abandoned and incapable of defending her dignity.

[2] Stratton (1992, 71-74) uses the expression "acute and chronic" suffering. Acute suffering exceeds and is related to an acute event, illness, pain or psychological manifestations. Chronic suffering is related more to the patient's situation as a whole.

[3] Starck (1992) observes that among older patients there are two categories: those who don't suffer but want attention, and those who actually suffer. The tendency to react to suffering and to alleviate it is related to how one perceives it. The suffering of the aged in institutions has been investigated in many studies in spite of the fact that one has not directly used the concept of suffering. We find it in Astrid Norberg's studies of demented patients. Nores (1993) alludes to older institutionalized patients having several forms of suffering.

[4] Descriptions are taken from the research studies made in 1990-91 at the Department of Caring Science and from the writings of patients and their relatives.

[5] The analysis of the concept of dignity is founded in the following sources: *Dictionary of the Swedish Language*, Bonnier's *Swedish Dictionary* 2nd edition, and *Synonym Dictionary*. The English word dignity means "true worth" or "the quality that earns or deserves respect," as well as the meaning of "high or honorable rank, post, or title" (Hornby, 1974) *Oxford Advanced Learner's Dictionary of Current English*.

[6] See Irene von Post's 1993 study, *Caregivers' Experiences of Dignity and Value Conflicts in Patient Care.*

[7] *Paralysis* (Åhgren, 1986) is the story of a man, Carl-Erik, 57 years old, who is stricken one night with an illness that leaves him totally paralyzed and, in addition, with expressive aphasia. There is nothing wrong with his sight, hearing or understanding.

[8] See Halldorsdottir (1993) Caring or Uncaring? An Important Question from the Perspective of the Recipient of Nursing and Health Care. The five modes of being with the patient that Halldorsdottir describes are: 1. Life destroying (biocidal), 2. Life limiting (biostatic), 3. Life neutral (biopassive), 4. Life supporting (bioactive), and 5. Life giving (biogenetic.)

[9] Students at the end of their education were asked to give a description of suffering in caring that they experienced in patient care during their education. All students said they had experienced suffering in caring, that is, suffering that was directly caused by caring.

[10] Bergbom-Engberg (1991,1993) has examined the phenomenon of "giving up" among patients on respirators and indicates that the relationship between the caregiver and the patient is crucial. A caregiver can cause the patient to give up.

[11] The discussion of questions about active or passive euthanasia falls outside the scope of this book. A great deal of material is available. See Ulla Qvarnström's book *Our Death*, 1993.

Chapter Twelve

From Illness to Suffering – The New Paradigm

In this closing chapter I shall pause and reflect before the challenges that caring science faces in the immediate future. Many things point to the fact that we are in, or at the beginning of, a paradigm shift in the science of caring as well as medicine. By a paradigm shift I mean that there is an exchange of the theoretical core, or in other words, we confront a change in the view of the reality of and the scientific knowledge of caring. More simply, we could say that the focus has moved from the diagnosis of illness and symptoms, to suffering and the suffering human being. There is an entirely new interest in the problem of suffering, which can be seen in the current discussions in both scientific and general literature. To re-introduce the concept of suffering involves essentially a return to the fundamental historic presuppositions for all caring.

Under the title *What is Humanism?* Alf Ahlberg writes (1950, 21):

> In our reasoning and debates we often use words and concepts without clearly stating their meaning. This is very comfortable, because depending on the situation we can give either one meaning or another to them…if one wants a truly fruitful debate one must, as Socrates said, "agree on what every thing is."

Ahlberg's formulation is significant in the discussion about changes in both caring and caring education. For more than a decade there has been eagerness to emphasize the humanistic perspective within caring education, and one has spoken on a more or less diffuse and general level. Through reasoning about the necessity of a humanistic dimension in caring one has felt something to be lacking. The debate has not been productive, and we have not succeeded in agreeing on what humanism is and above all, on what humanism concretely means within caring and caring education.

Jansson (1990) thinks that secular humanism, regardless of the form in which it is presented, is insufficient if we want to make room for the suffering human being to be reconciled to her existence and able to live as fully worthy a life as possible. He sees Christian ideas as a form of humanism but with a different historic origin than secular humanistic ideas, not necessarily in opposition to them. He emphasizes two specific sides of the Christian interpretation of life as essential for caring. The first is the requirement of love, i.e., love for my neighbor. The way of relating to other people becomes a central question, and with that even the entire worldview is changed. The second question, a unique feature of

Christianity, is taking negative elements in one's existence, such as suffering, illness and frailty, and using them as building stones that ultimately contribute to the good. This has to do with forgiveness and grace. Jansson believes that the Christian worldview in one way is more realistic in that it also considers the dark sides of life. At the same time we know that many people may have difficulty assimilating and accepting the Christian perspective.

Our worldview has been changed through various syntheses (actually theses and antitheses) that have succeeded each other with varying time intervals. The same may be said about the humanistic traditions. The first synthesis in modern times was the meeting between the Greek cultural school of thought and Christianity. The second great synthesis was the meeting of Augustine and medieval humanism (Ahlberg, 1950). Von Wright (1987) believes that we now stand before a new synthesis where facts and values can again be united.

The View of Reality

The question of what constitutes the starting point for caring has its basis in our view of reality. Today we have a distorted view of reality within caring. The image has been formed in an all too high degree by a reductionistic view of the human being and an overconfidence in technology. Johannison (1992) asserts that it is the medical-technical domination over all caring, having continued since the beginning of the 1800s, which has resulted in suffering being deprived of all its cultural context of meaning, and thereby technologized and rendered anonymous. We must return to the question of what caring actually means and what should constitute the fundamental interests of caring and caring science.

Cassell[2] believes that it is suffering and the suffering human being that constitute the primary focus of concern for medical science. This way of approaching medicine's field of knowledge comes close to that of caring science, although there are differences in perspective. It is the question of meaning that is central for the human sciences.[3] If we follow Cassell, the context of meaning in medicine can be interpreted as the suffering person's relationship with her own illness. The illness is not seen as an isolated phenomenon but in the context of a wider horizon of understanding that comprises the entire individual. The context of meaning of caring science consists of the suffering human being in relation to health, suffering and the whole life situation. The primary mission of caring is to help the human being to live despite suffering and illness, and with all available means to alleviate suffering. The differences in perspective can many times appear to be subtle and in clinical work it can be difficult to differentiate them. However, in a theoretical perspective one can see clear differences, which above all, may be seen in different research interests and methods, and in the development of theories.

The View of Knowledge

Interest in human suffering is related to our view of knowledge, i.e., our understanding of what we can and should obtain knowledge about, and the methods by which we can attain it. Tranøy[4] considers that the striking characteristic within the humanistic sciences is their dual nature. They contain both a historical and a systematic theoretical component. The systematic theoretical component includes, among others, the question of language.

The dominant approach and method of humanistic science consists of hermeneutics, or interpretation. Both the science of caring and medicine as science have been, to a great degree, ahistoric. The historic context of meaning, for example, the view of how caring has developed, has been lacking and the context of meaning has been confined to the here and now. Berdjajev[5] states that with an ahistoric viewpoint, culture is reduced to civilization and quality is replaced by quantity. People are then more oriented toward the means for life than toward life itself. Today, for example, we lack terms that describe human suffering.

The New Paradigm

"Reality is given to the human spirit as a great riddle. All individual sciences contribute to its determination."

Paulsen 1904

The new paradigm, if it is to have the power to succeed, must comprise all areas including clinical practice, education, and research. The point of departure for the new caring paradigm is that we must discover and re-shape the reality that the paradigm encompasses. This implies that we return to the idea of caring, its origin, and its historic presuppositions. The new paradigm presupposes a widening of the interdisciplinary field in both education and research. In order to learn to interpret the complex reality of caring, we need close cooperation with such areas as philosophy, theology, linguistics, anthropology, history of ideas, and the science of the fine arts. This demands a prioritizing of basic research in the near future.

What Does The New Paradigm Mean?

The new paradigm can be summarized in the following points:

1. The starting point is the suffering human being in relation to health. This provides deeper presuppositions for comprehensive caring.
2. The new paradigm also provides a basis for an ethic of caring where confirmation of the dignity of the human being as well as a deep responsibility for the other constitute the starting point.
3. Technology emerges in a deeper context of meaning and can therefore be adapted with regard to the individual person's desires and needs[6] and also includes values. In Kemp's words we are dealing with "technology-ethics."

Is This Possible?

As one views the person, so does one treat her.

Kemp 1991

I would like to direct the question of whether it is possible to carry out the new paradigm to all who, within some area, are responsible for caring. The most important thing is to have the courage to reflect about and accept the challenge that this implies. We must make the concepts penetrate our reality and transform it.

What then are the meaningful alternatives for the future? In the first place this is an ethical question. It deals with giving courage to young students, daring to allow them to be aware of their own view of life, and allowing them to act based on motives that seem true and good.

It does not involve primarily what subjects should be included in the curriculum, but more the attitudes and values that education should communicate. We can have a curriculum full of humanistic subjects, but that does not guarantee that we are nurturing future caregivers who have a humanistic attitude. Humanistic studies provide an essential foundation for education and reflection. But it is also important for caregivers to form their own context of meaning in caring and to develop their own criteria for evaluating what constitutes good care. In Ahlberg's words (1950, 31):

> All that violates human dignity, all that hinders and stifles human possibilities - however admirable and impressive it may seem from other points of view - is for humanism an evil. With this and only this criterion, the humanist must judge what is "progress" and "development" in historical life.

NOTES

[1] In my book *Bridges* I discuss what is implied in viewing the science of caring as a humanistic science. Within the international literature on the science of caring one perceives a growing interest in suffering as a phenomenon in caring. This is especially apparent in periodicals devoted to the science of caring. There are a number of theorists who emphasize suffering (e.g., Travelbee, 1970). Lanara in her doctoral thesis (1981) has made suffering her starting point and states that one of the noblest tasks of a nurse is to help the patient to accept her suffering. Taylor and Watson (1989) emphasize suffering in their book, *They Shall Not Hurt: Human Suffering and Human Caring*. They state that suffering is a general human phenomenon and emphasize the necessity of a humanistic science that goes beyond the objective and immediately given, to a deeper understanding of human suffering. In caring science discussions in the Nordic countries the question of suffering has not been especially prominent until the present. Can that be interpreted as an expression of the fact that we are still to a considerable degree fixed in the thinking grounded in the natural sciences?

Within medicine the discussion of suffering has been led by E.J. Cassell, doctor and professor. In 1981 he published an article in *The New England Journal of Medicine*, and in 1991 he published his book, *The Nature of Suffering and the Goals of Medicine*. Cassell's starting point is that the entire basis for medical practice, i.e., the view of illness, is insufficient and works against the goals of caring. The whole assumption that it is possible to identify, name, and treat illness apart from the ill person is erroneous. The doctor does not deal with the illness but with the ill individual. The Dane Juul Jensen (1983) is thinking along the same lines in his book, *Concepts of Illness in Practice*. In Sweden, Doctor Rolf Ahlzén has been conducting a discussion in the daily press about humanistic medical science. In Finland, I have not been able to trace a similar discussion, nor have I seen any evidence that this development has affected research.

[2] Cassell, ibid.

[3] Kasper (1981) connects the question of meaning with humanistic sciences and feels that it is the task of the humanistic sciences to take up questions of meaning, and to present meaningful alternatives for the planning of the future.

[4] See Tranøy (1983) "Humanistic Science—Individuality, Identity, and Possibilities of Legitimation," in Frängsmyr, T. (Ed.) *The Distinctive Character of the Humanities*. I do not go further in this connection into scientific-theoretical questions but refer the reader to the rich literature that is available in this area.

[5] When it concerns the historic dimensions see Berdjajev (1990), who has described the consequences of an ahistoric approach as the difference between culture and civilization.

[6] Kemp (1991) in his doctoral dissertation considers problems which emerge in connection with contemporary technologies. By "technology ethics" Kemp means the good technology, which does not reduce the other to an instrument but sets limits that both promises new possibilities for a richer existence and prohibits murder in our lives with others. Kemp's thesis is that we treat the other in conformity with how we understand him or her.

Epilogue

Eternity –
The Glory
of Suffering

The judgment was complete. The process had continued for eight years and the whole time he had been judged innocent. Now he was freed, and he read over and over again the eight lines that described the events of all these years. The description ended with the words, "He is free."

Never before during these years had he felt so captive,

never had his pain been so great as when he looked at these lines

wrath, hatred, abhorrence, revenge…the combined powers of evil

> *welled up within him*

the disappointment felt like a noose around his neck

he felt as though he were suffocating…

were these lines the reward for his suffering

that which should have been the triumph, the victory and the

> *other's contrition was suddenly nothing*

the universe stood still

in a few seconds the last battle of life and death had been played out

seconds became years

suddenly eternity stepped into the universe and in its dazzling light

> *everything paled*

dark became light

death became life

suffering became desire –

he fell down on his bare knees

he turned his head up towards heaven and thanked life

gave the devil a jaunty kick

the clown no longer needed to be a clown

the choice was his

and he chose life—love

liberation

the clown lay down quietly

turned his eyes up toward eternity and remained forever a

Star in the Milky Way

the bridge of Love.

REFERENCES

Ahlberg A. 1950. *Humanismen*. [Humanism]. Stockholm, Sweden: Sveriges Kyrkliga Studieförlag.

Ahlberg A. et al. 1987. *Latinsk-svensk ordbok*. [Latin-Swedish dictionary].(2nd edition). Stockholm, Sweden: Svenska bokförlaget.

Ahlin L. 1987. *Din livsfrukt*. [Your life's fruit]. Stockholm, Sweden: Bonniers.

Allén S. 1988. *Svensk Ord Bok*. [Swedish Dictionary]. (2nd edition). Compiled at Språkdata Göteborgs universitet. Keuru, Finland: Förlagsaktiebolaget OTAVA.

Aristotle 1987. *Om själen*. [On the Soul]. (Transl. J. Gabrielsson. Reprint of the edition from 1925). Göteborg, Sweden: Daidalos.

Benktson B-E. 1976. *Gränssituationerna. Frågan om livets mening i existensfilosofisk belysning*. [Borderline situations. The question about the meaning of life in the light of existential philosophy]. Lund, Sweden: Liber läromedel.

Berdjajev N. 1990. *Historiens mening: ett försök till en filosofi om det mänskliga ödet*. [The meaning of history: a suggestion to a philosophy about the human faith]. (Orig. title: Smyslistori, Berlin 1923). Skellefteå, Sweden: Artos.

Bergbom-Engberg I. 1991. Giving up and withdrawal by ventilator treated patients: Nurses' experience. *Intensive Care Nursing*, 1991, 7, 200-205.

Bergbom-Engberg I. 1993. The communication process with ventilator patients in the ICU as perceived by the nursing staff. *Intensive and Critical Care Nursing*, 1993, 9, 40-47.

Bergson H. 1912. *Tiden och den fria viljan*. [Time and the free will]. Stockholm, Sweden: Wahlström & Widstrand.

Bergson H. 1914. *Intuition och intelligens*. [Intuition and intelligence]. Stockholm, Sweden: Wahlström & Widstrand.

Bibeln [Bible]. 1917. Stockholm: Evangeliske Fosterlands-stiftelsens förlag.

Bible, New Revised Standard Version. 1989. Grand Rapids, Michigan: Zondervan Publishing House.

Boye, K. 1935. *För trädets skull*. [For the tree's sake]. Stockholm: Bonniers.

Brantschen J. 1988. *Miksi Jumala sallii kärsimyksen?* [Why does God allow suffering?]. Helsinki, Finland: Sley-Kirjat.

Buber M. 1989. *Skuld och skuldkänsla*. [Guilt and guilt feelings]. Ludvika, Sweden: Dualis förlag.

Cassell E.J. 1982. The nature of suffering and the goals of medicine. *The New England Journal of Medicine* 306, II, 639-645.

Cassell E.J. 1991. *The Nature of Suffering and the Goals of Medicine*. Oxford University Press.

Colliander T. 1987. *Motiv*. [Motives]. Stockholm, Sweden: Atlantis.

Dahl T. (ed.) 1949. *Svenska män och kvinnor. Biografisk uppslagsbok*. [Swedish men and women. Biographical encyclopedia]. Stockholm, Sweden: Albert Bonniers Förlag.

Dahl T. 1975. *När jag var sjuk*. [When I was ill]. Gothenburg, Sweden: Författarförlaget.

References

Dahlby F. 1963. *De heliga tecknens hemlighet. Symboler och attribut.* [The secret of the holy signs. Symbols and attributes]. Stockholm, Sweden: Diakonistyrelsen.

Dalin A.F. 1975. *Svenska språkets synonymer.* [Synonyms of the Swedish language]. Stockholm, Sweden: Liber Förlag.

Eckhart M. 1984. *Undervisande tal jämte andra texter.* [Didactic speeches and other texts]. Selection, translation and comments by B. Brisman. Reprint of the 1966 edition. Skellefteå, Sweden: Artos.

Eriksson K. 1976. *Hälsa – en teoretisk och begreppsanalytisk studie om hälsa och dess natur som mål för hälsovårdsedukation.* [Health – a theoretical and concept analysis study on health and its nature as a goal for health care education]. Licentiate's dissertation. Department of Education, University of Helsinki, Finland.

Eriksson K. 1989. *Hälsans idé.* [The idea of health]. (2nd edition.) Stockholm, Sweden: Almqvist & Wiksell.

Eriksson K. 1990. *Pro Caritate. En lägesbestämning av caritativ vård.* [Pro Caritate. The situation of caritative care]. Caring research 2/1990. Department of Caring Science, Åbo Akademi University, Finland.

Eriksson K. 1991. Att lindra lidande. [To alleviate suffering]. In: Eriksson K. & Barbosa da Silva A. (eds.) *Vårdteologi.* [Caring theology]. Caring research 3/1991. Department of Caring Science, Åbo Akademi University, Finland.

Eriksson K. 1992a. *Broar. Introduktion i vårdvetenskaplig metod.* [Bridges. Introduction to caring science method]. Department of Caring Science, Åbo Akademi University, Finland.

Eriksson K. 1992b. Nursing: The Caring Practice "Being There". In: Gaut D. (ed.) *The Presence of Caring in Nursing.* New York: National League for Nursing Press, pp. 201-210.

Eriksson K. & Herberts S. 1992. *Den mångdimensionella hälsan. En studie av hälsobilden hos sjukvårdsledare och sjukvårdspersonal.* [Multidimensional health. A study of the views of health among nurse executives and nursing staff]. Project report 2. The Nursing District of the Federation of Municipalities of Vasa and the Department of Caring Science, Åbo Akademi University, Finland.

Eriksson K. (ed.) 1993. *Möten med lidanden.* [Encounters with suffering]. Caring research 4/1993. The Department of Caring Science, Åbo Akademi University, Finland.

Eriksson K. & Herberts S. 1993. Lidande – en begreppsanalytisk studie. [Suffering – a concept analysis study]. In: Eriksson K. (ed.) 1993. *Möten med lidanden.* [Encounters with suffering]. Caring research 4/1993. The Department of Caring Science, Åbo Akademi University, Finland.

Fant M. 1991. *De sista åren.* [The last years]. Stockholm, Sweden: Natur och Kultur.

Farnham B. 1988. *Min Gud är stor.* [My God is great]. Örebro, Sweden: Libris.

Fjellbu A. 1941. *Lidandets mening.* [The meaning of suffering]. Stockholm, Sweden: Diakonistyrelsen.

Frankl V. 1974. *Livet måste ha en mening.* [Life must have a meaning]. (Orig. title from 1946: Ein Psychologe erlebt das Konzentrationslager.) Stockholm, Sweden: Aldus Bonniers.

Frankl V. 1986. *The doctor and the soul. From Psychotherapy to Logotherapy.* New York: Vintage Books.

Frankl V. 1990. *Psykiatern och själen*. [The doctor and the soul]. Stockholm, Sweden: Natur och Kultur.

Halldorsdottir S. 1993. *"Caring or Uncaring?": An Important Question from the Perspective of the Recipient of Nursing and Health Care*. Nordic jubilee symposium "To Care or not to Care – The Key Question in Nursing", The Department of Caring Science, Åbo Akademi University, Vasa, Finland, 24-25.5.1993.

Hellquist E. 1980. *Svensk etymologisk ordbok*. [Swedish etymological dictionary]. Lund, Sweden: Liber Läromedel.

Hill C.S., Jr. 1992. Suffering as contrasted to pain, loss, grief, despair and loneliness. In: Starck P.L. & McGovern J.P. (eds.). *Hidden Dimension of Illness: Human Suffering*. New York: National League for Nursing Press, pp. 69-80.

Hjelm G. 1960. *Lidandets mening*. [The meaning of suffering]. Örebro, Sweden: Evangelipress.

Hornby A.S. et al. 1974. *Oxford Advanced Learner's Dictionary of Current English*. London, England: Oxford University Press.

Huber M. 1946. *Den barmhärtige samariten*. [The Good Samaritan]. Stockholm, Sweden: Svenska Kyrkans Diakonistyrelses Bokförlag.

Illustrerat bibellexikon. [Illustrated Bible Dictionary].1967. Odeberg H. & Gilbrant T. (eds.) Bergen, Norway: Eide.

Jansson J-M. 1990. *Diskussionsinlägg inom forskarutbildningen i vårdvetenskap vid Institutionen för vårdvetenskap*. [Contribution to the discussion about the postgraduate studies at the Department of Caring Science]. Vasa, Finland: Åbo Akademi University.

Jensen J. 1983. *Sjukdomsbegrepp i praktiken*. [Concepts of illness in practice]. Solna, Sweden: Esselte studium.

Johannisson K. 1992. Att lida och fördraga. [To suffer and endure]. In: Kallenberg K. (ed.) *Lidandets mening*. [The meaning of suffering]. Stockholm, Sweden: Natur och Kultur, pp. 112-123.

Juchli L. 1991. *Heilen durch wiederdecken der Ganzheit*. Nordic Caring Science Conference: Caritas & Passio, 27-29.5.1991. The Department of Caring Science, Åbo Akademi University, Finland.

Jung C.G. 1981. *The Collected Works of C.G. Jung*. (Orig. title: Die Gesammelten Werke von C.G. Jung.) Read H. & Fordham M. & Adler G. (eds.) Volume II. Psychology and Religion: West and East. London & Henley: Routledge & Kegan.

Jung C.G. 1993. *Kärsimyksestä*. (On Suffering) Helsinki: Kirjayntymä.

Kallenberg K. (ed.) 1992. *Lidandets mening*. [The meaning of suffering]. Stockholm, Sweden: Natur och Kultur.

Kasper W. 1981. *Introduktion till den kristna tron*. [Introduction to the Christian faith]. Uppsala, Sweden: Katolska Bokförlaget.

Kemp P. 1991. *Det oersättliga. En teknologietik*. [The irreplaceable. The ethics of technology]. Stockholm, Sweden: Symposium.

Kierkegaard S. 1928. *Søren Kierkegaards Dagbok*. [The Diary of Søren Kierkegaard]. Stockholm, Sweden: Svenska Kyrkans Diakonistyrelses Bokförlag.

Kierkegaard S. 1963. (orig. edition 1844). *Begreppet Ångest*. [The Concept of Anxiety]. Helsinki, Finland: Holger Schildts Förlag.

Kierkegaard S. 1939. *Övning i Kristendom*. [Practice of Christianity]. Stockholm, Sweden: Svenska Kyrkans Diakonistyrelses Bokförlag.

References

Kübler-Ross E. 1972. *Samtal inför döden*. [Conversations before death]. Stockholm, Sweden: Bonniers.

Lanara V. 1981. *Heroism as a Nursing Value. A Philosophical Perspective*. Athens, Greece: Publications of Sisterhood Evniki.

Lazare A. 1992. The suffering of shame and humiliation in illness. In: Starck P.L. & McGovern J.P. (eds.) *Hidden Dimension of Illness: Human Suffering*. New York: National League for Nursing Press, pp. 227-244.

Lewis C.S. 1955. *Lidandets problem*. [The problem of pain]. Malmö, Sweden: Gleerups förlag.

Lindblom L. 1940. *Boken om Job och hans lidande*. [The book about Job and his suffering]. Lund, Sweden: Gleerups.

Lindholm L. & Eriksson K. 1993a. *Lidande och kärlek ur ett psykiatriskt perspektiv - en case studie av mötet mellan mänskligt lidande och kärlek*. [Suffering and love from a psychiatric perspective - a case study of the encounter between human suffering and love]. In: Eriksson K. (ed.) 1993. *Möten med lidanden*. [Encounters with suffering]. Caring research 4/1993. The Department of Caring Science, Åbo Akademi University, Finland.

Lindholm L. & Eriksson K. 1993b. To understand and alleviate suffering in a caring culture. *Journal of Advanced Nursing*, 1993, 18, 1354-1361.

Ljunglund L. 1914. *Lifvets bejakande. Några tankar om viljan och kärleken*. [To have a positive outlook on life. Some thoughts about will and love]. Stockholm, Sweden: Wahlström & Widstrand.

Malmberg T. 1980. *Human Territoriality*. Stockholm, Sweden: Liber Förlag.

Malmström S., Györki I. & Sjögren P.A. 1991. *Bonniers svenska ordbok*. [Bonnier's Swedish Dictionary]. (5th edition). Stockholm, Sweden: Bonniers.

May R. 1972. *Makt och oskuld*. [Power and innocence]. Stockholm, Sweden: Aldus.

May R. 1988. *Modet att skapa*. [The courage to create]. Stockholm, Sweden: Bonnier Fakta.

Nightingale F. (1859) 1954. *Anteckningar om sjukvård*. [Orig. title: Notes on nursing. What it is and what it is not]. Stockholm, Sweden: Svensk sjuksköterskeförenings förlag.

Nordenfelt L. 1991. *Livskvalitet och hälsa*. [Quality of life and health]. Stockholm, Sweden: Almqvist & Wiksell.

Nores T. 1992. *Olemassaolokokemus. Naisvanhuspotilaan olemassaolokokemusta koskeva käsitteellinen ja empiirinen analyysi*. [The experience of existing. An analytical and empirical analysis of the older woman patient's experience of existing.] Doctoral dissertation. Department of Nursing, University of Turku, Finland.

Nygren A. 1932. *Försoningen*. [Reconciliation]. Stockholm, Sweden: Sveriges Kristliga Studentrörelses Bokförlag.

Ordbok över svenska språket. [Dictionary of the Swedish language]. 1942. Lund, Sweden: Svenska Akademien.

Pauli E. 1930. *Den vardande människan*. [The becoming human being]. Twelve lectures. Stockholm, Sweden: Birkagårdens förlag.

Pauli E. 1938. *Kamp eller Resignation*. [Struggle or Resignation]. Copenhagen, Denmark: Hagerup.

Paulsen F. 1904. *De metafysiska problemen. Inledning till filosofien*. [Metaphysical problems. An introduction to philosophy]. Stockholm, Sweden: Bonniers.

Qvarnström U. 1993. *Vår död.* [Our death]. Stockholm, Sweden: Almqvist & Wiksell.

Richter H.E. (ed.). 1979. *Från allmakt till vanmakt.* [From omnipotence to impotence]. Stockholm, Sweden: Norstedts.

Rousseau J.J. 1978. *Emilie II eller Om uppfostran.* [Emilie II or About upbringing]. Gothenburg, Sweden: Stegelands.

Sachs L. 1992. Lidandet som kommunikation - ett mänskligt fenomen sett i kulturella sammanhang. [Suffering as a way of communication - a human phenomenon seen in different cultural situations]. In: Kallenberg K. (ed.) 1992. *Lidandets mening.* [The meaning of suffering]. Stockholm, Sweden: Natur och Kultur.

SAOB-arkivmaterial. [SAOB archive material]. The collections of the Dictionary of the Swedish Academy. Lund, Sweden: C.W.K. Gleerups Förlag.

SAOB. Ordbok över svenska språket. [SAOB. Dictionary of the Swedish language]. Published by the Swedish Academy. Lund, Sweden.

Schopenhauer A. 1905. *Tankar och fragment.* [Thoughts and fragments]. Stockholm, Sweden: Bonniers.

Seiler H. 1989. *Jesus Kristus i Tiden.* [Jesus Christ in Time]. Uppsala, Sweden: Katolska Bokförlaget.

Siegel B.S. 1990. *Kärlek, Tro och Helande.* [Love, Faith and Healing]. Stockholm, Sweden: Bonnier Fakta.

Silbersky L. & Svedelid O. 1992. *Och tiden den stod stilla.* [And time stood still]. Stockholm, Sweden: Sellin & Partner.

Stanley J.E. 1934. *Kristus och det mänskliga lidandet.* [Christ and Human Suffering]. Stockholm, Sweden: Svenska Tryckeriaktiebolaget.

Starck P. 1992. The management of suffering in a nursing home: An ethnographic study. In: Starck P.L. & McGovern J.P. (eds.) *Hidden Dimension of Illness: Human Suffering.* New York: National League for Nursing Press, pp. 127-154.

Starck P.L. & McGovern J.P. (eds.) 1992. *Hidden Dimension of Illness: Human Suffering.* New York: National League for Nursing Press.

Stinissen W. 1990. *Natten är mitt ljus.* [The night is my light]. Serie KARMEL, nr 23. Tågarp: Glunslöv: Karmeliterna.

Stott J. 1986. *Korset - Meningen med Jesu död.* [Orig. title: The Cross of Christ]. Örebro, Sweden: Libris.

Strömberg A. 1984. *Stora Synonymordboken.* [The Comprehensive Dictionary of Synonyms]. Stockholm, Sweden: Strömbergs.

Studiebibeln. Band V. [The study bible. Volume V]. Stockholm, Sweden: Normans förlag.

Svenska Akademiens källförteckning och dess supplement. [The bibliography of the Swedish Academy and its supplements]. 1975. Lund, Sweden: P.H. & Lindstedts Universitetsbokhandel.

Taylor R.L. & Watson J. 1989. *They Shall Not Hurt. Human Suffering and Human Caring.* Boulder, Colorado: Colorado Associated University Press.

Topor A. 1992. Lidandets mening. [The meaning of suffering]. In: Kallenberg K. (ed.) *Lidandets mening.* [The meaning of suffering]. Stockholm, Sweden: Natur och Kultur.

Tournier P. 1983. *En plats för dig. Om människans sökande efter sina rötter.* [A place for you. About man's search for his roots]. Örebro, Sweden: Libris.

References

Tranøy K. E. 1983. *Humanistisk vitenskap - egenart, identitet och legitimer-ingsmuligheter.* [Humanistic science - character, identity and possibilities of legitimacy]. In: Frängsmyr T. (ed.) *Humanioras egenart.* [The distinctive character of the humanities]. Oslo, Norway: Universitetsforlaget.

Travelbee J. 1969. *Intervention in Psychiatric Nursing. Process in the One to One Relationship.* Philadelphia: FA Davis Company.

Vonhoff H. 1962. *I kamp mot nöd. Barmhärtighetens historia.* [The struggle against need. The history of mercy]. Stockholm, Sweden: EFS-Förlag.

von Post I. 1993. *Vårdares upplevelser av värdighet och värdekonflikter i patientvården.* [Caregivers' experiences of dignity and value conflicts in patient care]. Master's thesis. The Department of Caring Science, Åbo Akademi University, Finland.

von Wright G.H. 1987. *Vetenskapen och förnuftet.* [Science and reason]. Stockholm, Sweden: Bonniers.

Wikström O. 1990. *Den outgrundliga människan.* [The inscrutable human being]. Stockholm, Sweden: Natur och Kultur.

Åhgren C.E. 1986. *Förlamningen. Dagboksanteckningar.* [Paralysis. Notes in a diary]. Växjö, Sweden: Lic Förlag and Landstingsförbundet.

Åkerberg H. 1987. *"Livet som utmaning" - existentiell ångest hos svenska gymnasieelever.* ["Life as a challenge" - existential anxiety among Swedish upper secondary school pupils]. Stockholm, Sweden: Norstedts.

INDEX

Index